Written & Designed by

Annie Kelly & Andy Howe

AlienZulu

© ANDY HOWE & ANNIE KELLY 2004
All rights reserved

Published by:
Take Two
1 Red Lodge, South Hill Ave
Harrow on the Hill
Middx HA1 3NZ

www.alienzulu.co.uk

The rights of Andy Howe and Annie Kelly to be identified as the authors of this work has been asserted by them in accordance with the Copyright, Designs and Patents act 1988.

Cover design: © ANDY HOWE & ANNIE KELLY 2004

A CIP record of this book is available from the British Library.

First printed June 2004

Reprinted 2005

ISBN 0-9547677-0-5

Printed in Great Britain by TJ International Ltd, Padstow, Cornwall

THANKYOU

Thanks to everyone at the Old Gaytonians RFC where I learned to play the game some 25 years ago under the firm but fair chairmanship of (Admiral) Dave Jones.

Thanks also to the gentlemen of The COFB golf society and almost everyone I have ever been skiing with for keeping the game alive all these years and contributing a number of superb categories. More recently, during the compiling of this book, a big thank you to both staff and regulars at CafeCafe on Harrow-on-the-Hill for hours of in-depth research, late nights and the inevitable hangovers.

Andy Howe

www.alienzulu.co.uk

how to play

getting started - the basic game

The game can be played by any number of people from one upwards. The rules are flexible but the basic idea is simple.

First, pick a category. If you haven't played before then start at the beginning of the book with 'Alien Zulu'. Each category page contains a short introduction and some sample answers to give you an idea of what you are looking for. You should read this out to everyone before you begin.

Whoever chooses the category goes first. You then go round clockwise in turn, each person giving an answer that fits into the chosen category. If a player can't think of an answer, gives an incorrect answer or repeats an answer they are out. However, if you want to keep the game going longer or the category is really difficult you could give everyone three lives. Whatever you decide the last person left in is the winner.

Each category in the book is followed by a list of answers. You should only look at these when the game is over or if you are really stuck and need some inspiration.

how to play

what does this mean? -

You will notice that every category page includes this circular symbol. This tells you the number of answers we have included in the book for that particular category.

Whilst we have done a lot of research to confirm details, check spellings etc. we have only included answers in this book that we have found by actually playing the game ourselves. It is, therefore, important to remember that the answers we have included are not a definitive list but are there to give you inspiration if you get stuck.

When choosing a category you can use these numbers as a kind of grading system because they do, in some way, reflect the difficulty of that category. Obviously the higher the number the more answers we have found and so, in theory, the easier it should be.

If you are playing the game on your own, these are the numbers to beat.

how to play

what does this mean? - ABC

Some of the simpler categories in the book can be made more challenging by doing them alphabetically. This means that player one has to give an answer beginning with A, player two must then think of an answer beginning with B, and so on until you get to Z.

We have only used the ABC symbol on categories where we have found at least one answer for 20 or more letters of the alphabet. X, Y and Z are, of course, always going to be difficult so you may want to group these together as one letter for the purposes of this game.

If you cannot think of an answer in an alphabetical game the letter is thrown open to the rest of the players. If no one can think of a correct answer you are not penalised but move on to the next letter. If, however, any of the other players can come up with a correct answer you do a forfeit, lose a life, or get knocked out in the usual way.

how to play

some simple rules

RIGHT OR WRONG

If an answer is disputed, the player concerned should be allowed to argue their case, after which it should be put to the vote. If you can get away with an incorrect answer by bluffing, that is perfectly acceptable, sometimes a clever or amusing answer can be as good as a correct one, so keep an open mind.

TIME LIMITS

The game should be played at a reasonable pace otherwise people will start getting bored. There is no official time limit but 'a quick game is a good game' and this simple rule should be adhered to and quoted as often as possible when things are running a little slow.

GOING SOLO

If you are playing the game on your own, you should probably get out more, however, it is a great way of killing time on a long journey or just relaxing on holiday. The alphabet games are particularly good for this, try getting from A-Z without passing or why not try beating the book.

how to play

The numbers on the category pages are the numbers to beat and you can use the notes pages at the back of the book to write down your answers.

DRINKING FORFEITS

Drinking forfeits, while not essential, will really liven things up and add a whole new dimension to the game. What you drink and how much you drink is up to you, but something appropriate to the occasion is always a good idea. Shots of ice cold vodka at a dinner party, schnapps in a ski chalet, Margaritas round the pool, the choice is yours.

The Basic Game - Pick a category and start playing as normal. In this version of the game, however, if you cannot think of an answer, repeat or give an incorrect answer, you must drink a forfeit before being knocked out. The last person left in is the winner.

Shot in the Dark - This is played exactly the same way as the basic game except that the drinks in the middle need a little more preparation. Choose a drink like vodka and orange for the forfeit. Fill half the glasses with both vodka and orange juice and half with just orange juice. To avoid cheating one person should mix the drinks and another should shuffle them around so no one knows which is which. As you get knocked out you choose one of the drinks from the ever decreasing selection left in the middle and hope for the best.

Shoot Out - Perhaps the best way to play the game, although not for the faint hearted. In this game there is no escape, you cannot get knocked out or lose a life, instead if you make a mistake you must take your punishment however often it comes around. The game is only over when three players in a row are unable to think of a correct answer and at that point anyone left in is a winner, and usually very pleased about it too.

Hot Shot - A great game for two people. In this game you sit opposite your opponent with a single drink in the middle. Pick a category and take it in turns to answer, any mistake and you must drink the forfeit, refill the glass, choose a new category and start again. Make sure you play this game at a good pace, ten seconds should be ample time to think of an answer. The game ends when either one of you surrenders.

categories

categories

categories

categories

alien zulu

It is amazing just how many films there are with only one word in the title, Hitchcock alone made over fifteen of them. We have included over eighty films in our list of answers but there are many more. How many can you think of? Remember that one word title means ONE word title, so films like 'The Exorcist' or 'The Abyss' are not allowed.

If you want to make things a little more difficult then this is a really good category to do alphabetically, we have found at least one film for every letter from Alien to Zulu.

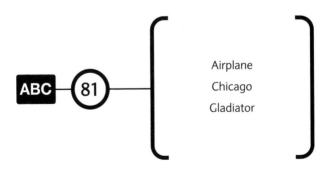

ABC (81)

Airplane
Chicago
Gladiator

Airport	Gigi	Pocahontas
Alfie	Goodfellas	Porkys
Alien	Grease	Predator
Amadeus	Gremlins	Psycho
Arthur	Halloween	Quadrophenia
Babe	Harvey	Reds
Bambi	Hook	Rocky
Batman	Insomnia	Seven
Beetlejuice	Iris	Shaft
Big	Jaws	Shampoo
Braveheart	Jezebel	Shrek
Bugsy	Klute	Signs
Bullitt	K-Pax	Spiderman
Cabaret	Lolita	Thunderball
Carrie	Leon	Titanic
Casablanca	Manhattan	Tootsie
Casino	Misery	Traffic
Clueless	Moonstruck	Twins
Cocoon	Mulan	Unforgiven
Deliverance	Notorious	Vertigo
Disclosure	Network	Westworld
Earthquake	Oklahoma	Witness
Fantasia	Oliver	X-men
Fargo	Parenthood	Yentl
Ghost	Patton	Zorro
Giant	Platoon	Zulu

three of a kind

How many things can you think of that always come in threes? As you can see, with some creative thinking, we have come up with well over sixty answers.

Remember, as well as physical things, like cricket stumps or legs on a tripod, it is perfectly acceptable to have more abstract, even fictitious, answers as long as they are universally recognised as always coming in threes, for example, Three Blind Mice.

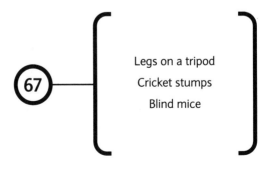

67

Legs on a tripod
Cricket stumps
Blind mice

three of a kind

A crowd	*Two's company*
A set of darts	*One hundred and eighty!*
Ages of Man	*A painting by Titian*
Amigos	*Steve Martin and friends*
Bad things	*Why do they always come in threes?*
Balls on a billiard table	*Red, white and spot*
Balls on a pawnbroker sign	*Pop goes the weasel*
Bears in the fairy story	*Who's been sleeping in my bed?*
Books in a trilogy	*Lord of the Rings*
Cards in a three card trick	*Don't brag if you get one*
Charlie's Angels	*Farah Fawcett and the rest*
Cheers	*Hip, hip hooray*
Columbus's ships	*Nina, Pinta and Santa Maria*
Colours in traffic lights	*Red, amber and green*
Coins in a fountain	*Romance in Rome*
Corners on a triangle	*Basic geometry*
Degrees	*Prince Charles should get this one*
Dimensions	*3D*
Dog Night	*70's pop group*
Events in a triathlon	*Running, swimming and cycling*
Feet in a yard	*That's 0.9144 of a metre to you*
French hens	*Two turtle doves*
Goals in hat trick	*Or tries or wickets*
Holes in a bowling ball	*Strike!*
Hulls on a trimaran	*One more than a catamaran*
Laws of motion	*Isaac Newton*

Leaves on a clover . . . . *Unlucky for some*

Legged race . . . . *Just like Jake the Peg*

Legs on Jake the Peg . . . .*Vintage Rolf Harris*

Lions on your chest . . . .*Come on England!*

Little Maids from School . . . . *Song from the Mikado*

Little pigs . . . .*I'll huff and I'll puff*

Men and a Baby . . . . *Selleck, Guttenberg and Danson*

Men in a Boat . . . .*Book by Jerome K. Jerome*

Ménage a trois . . . . *When three isn't a crowd*

Musketeers . . . . *Porthos, Athos & Aramis*

Officials on a football pitch . . . .*Ref and two linesmen*

Parts of a harmony . . . . *Three part harmony*

Picture cards . . . .*King, Queen, Jack*

Pins on a plug. . . . .*13 amp*

Players in a trio . . . .*Emerson, Lake and Palmer*

Points on a trident . . . .*Ask Neptune*

Primary colours . . . . *Red, blue and yellow*

Rings in a circus . . . . *Send in the clowns*

Saints . . . . *Faith, Hope and Charity*

Sides of a triangle. . . . .*More basic geometry*

Sofas and chairs . . . .*Three piece suite*

Steps to heaven . . . . *Showaddywaddy*

Stooges . . . .*Larry, Curly and Moe*

Strikes and you're out . . . .*Baseball*

Tenors . . . . *Domingo, Pavarotti and Carreras*

The R's . . . .*Reading, writing and arithmetic?*

three of a kind

Times a Lady . . . .*The Commodores*

Toes on a sloth . . . . *A three toed sloth that is*

Trinities . . . .*Father, son & holy ghost*

Triple jump . . . .*Hop, skip and a jump*

Triplets . . . . *Babies or musical notes*

Types of matter. . . . .*Animal, vegetable or mineral*

Victories in a Triple Crown . . . . .*Rugby home internationals*

Wishes . . . .*Aladdin and his magic lantern*

Wise men . . . . *Caspar, Melchior and Balthasar*

Wheels on a Reliant Robin . . . .*Just like Del boy*

Witches in Macbeth. . . . . . . *Hubble bubble, toil and trouble*

Wrongs . . . .*Don't make a right*

watching the detectives

How many TV crime fighters can you remember? There are plenty to choose from so make sure you get full names, where commonly used, plus the show they appeared in for a correct answer.

On a series like 'Hill Street Blues' that has a big cast we have only listed one or two of the better known characters but, of course, any correct name is ok. Where there is an inseparable double act like Daziel & Pascoe you can either count each name separately or require both for a correct answer.

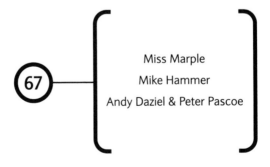

67
Miss Marple
Mike Hammer
Andy Daziel & Peter Pascoe

watching the detectives

J L McCabe & Jake Styles . . . . *Jake and the Fatman*

Jason King . . . . *Jason King*

Inspt Jean D'Arblay . . . . *Juliet Bravo*

Theo Kojak . . . . *Kojak*

Lennie Briscoe, Ed Green. . . . . *Law & Order*

Thomas Magnum . . . . *Magnum*

Sam McCloud . . . . *McCloud*

Stewart McMillan . . . . *McMillan and Wife*

Susan Blake, Jim Oulton. . . . . *Merseybeat*

James "Sonny" Crokett & Ricardo Tubbs . . . . *Miami Vice*

Tom Barnaby & Gavin Troy . . . . *Midsomer Murders*

Adrian Monk. . . . . *Monk*

Inspector Morse & Lewis . . . . *Morse*

Maddie Hayes & David Addison . . . . *Moonlighting*

Jessica Fletcher . . . . *Murder She Wrote*

Andy Sipowicz, Bobby Simone. . . . . *NYPD Blue*

Perry Mason . . . . *Perry Mason*

Hercule Poirot. . . . . *Poirot*

Jane Tennison . . . . *Prime Suspect*

Jeff Randall & Marty Hopkirk . . . *Randall and Hopkirk Deceased*

Jim Rockford . . . . *The Rockford Files*

Quincy. . . . . *Quincy MD*

Remington Steele . . . . *Remington Steele*

Sapphire and Steele. . . . . *Sapphire and Steele*

Vic Mackey, Claudette Wyms . . . . *The Shield*

Eddie Shoestring . . . . *Shoestring*

watching the detectives

Sam Ryan . . . . *Silent Witness*

Charlie Barlow . . . . *Softly Softly*

David Starsky & Ken Hutchinson . . . . *Starsky & Hutch*

Mike Stone & Steve Keller . . . . *Streets of San Francisco*

Jack Regan & George Carter . . . . *The Sweeny*

Jim Taggart . . . . *Taggart*

T J Hooker . . . . *T J Hooker*

Jack Frost . . . . *Touch of Frost*

Elliott Ness . . . . *The Untouchables*

Van Der Valk . . . . *Van der Valk*

Peter Boyd, Grace Foley . . . . *Waking the Dead*

John Watt, Bert Lynch. . . . . *Z Cars*

dr doolittle

A chance to talk to the animals, or at least sound like them, this could end up a noisy game!

The idea is to come up with as many different animal sounds as you can. If there is any debate on which noise belongs to which animal, or indeed, if the noise belongs to an animal at all, you should put it to the vote. Either way an impression of the sound in question is mandatory for any dubious answers.

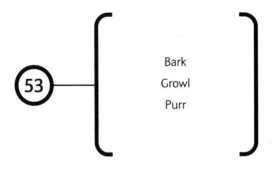

53 {
Bark
Growl
Purr
}

dr doolittle

Baa	*Sheep*	Howl	*Wolf*
Bell	*Stag*	Laugh	*Hyena*
Bellow	*Bull*	Low	*Cattle*
Bleat	*Goat*	Meow	*Cat*
Boom	*Bittern*	Moan	*Dove*
Bray	*Donkey*	Moo	*Cow*
Buzz	*Bee*	Neigh	*Horse*
Cackle	*Goose*	Pipe	*Sandpiper*
Caterwaul	*Tom Cat*	Quack	*Duck*
Caw	*Crow*	Roar	*Lion*
Chatter	*Monkey*	Scream	*Eagle*
Cheep	*Chick*	Screech	*Owl*
Chirp	*Sparrow*	Snort	*Rhinoceros*
Click	*Dolphin*	Squawk	*Gull*
Cluck	*Hen*	Squeak	*Mouse*
Coo	*Pigeon*	Squeal	*Piglet*
Croak	*Frog*	Talk	*Parrot*
Cry	*Guinea Fowl*	Trumpet	*Elephant*
Cuckoo	*Cuckoo*	Tweet	*Bird*
Drone	*Beetle*	Warble	*Nightingale*
Drum	*Grouse*	Whinny	*Horse*
Gobble	*Turkey*	Whistle	*Blackbird*
Grunt	*Pig*	Woof	*Dog*
Hiss	*Snake*	Yelp	*Fox*
Honk	*Goose*		
Hoot	*Owl*		

singing the blues

All the songs in this category have a colour in their title.

A song like 'I Can Sing A Rainbow', perhaps the ultimate colour song, has plenty of colours in the lyrics but none in the title, so is not allowed.

Depending on the people you are playing with and how much you've had to drink you might want to ask people to sing at least one line from the song when they answer.

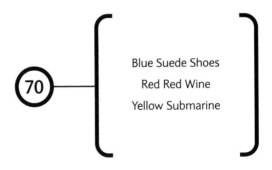

(70)

Blue Suede Shoes
Red Red Wine
Yellow Submarine

singing the blues

---

99 Red Balloons. . . . . *Nena*

Bad Bad Leroy Brown. . . . . *Jim Croce*

Big Yellow Taxi . . . . *Joni Mitchell*

Black Betty. . . . . *Ram Jam*

Black is Black . . . . *La Belle Epoque*

Black Magic Woman . . . . *Santana*

Black Man Ray . . . . *China Crisis*

Black or White . . . . *Michael Jackson*

Black Pearl . . . . *Horace Faith*

Blue Bayou. . . . .*Linda Rondstat*

Blue Christmas. . . . . *Elvis Presley*

Blue Guitar. . . . . *Justin Hayward*

Blue Eyes. . . . .*Elton John*

Blue Monday. . . . .*New Order*

Blue Moon. . . . . *Showaddywaddy*

Blue Velvet. . . . .*Bobby Vinton*

Brown Eyed Girl. . . . .*Van Morrison*

Brown Girl in the Ring. . . . .*Boney M*

Brown Sugar. . . . . *Rolling Stones*

Don't It Make My Brown Eyes Blue. . . . . *Crystal Gayle*

Gold. . . . .*Spandau Ballet*

Golden Brown. . . . .*The Stranglers*

Goodbye Yellow Brick Road. . . . . *Elton John*

Green Door. . . . . *Shakin' Stevens*

Green Green Grass of Home. . . . . *Tom Jones*

Green Onions. . . . . *Booker T and the MGs*

Green Tambourine. . . . .*The Lemon Pipers*

Hi Ho Silver. . . . . *Jim Diamond*

Hi Ho Silver Lining. . . . . *Jeff Beck*

Lady In Red. . . . .*Chris de Burgh*

Lilac Wine. . . . . *Elkie Brooks*

Lily the Pink. . . . . *The Scaffold*

Little Brown Jug. . . . . *Glenn Miller*

Little Red Corvette. . . . . *Prince*

Little Red Rooster. . . . . *The Rolling Stones*

Little White Bull . . . . *Tommy Steele*

Mellow Yellow. . . . . *Donovan*

Men in Black. . . . .*Will Smith*

Moody Blue. . . . .*Elvis Presley*

Nights in White Satin. . . . .*Moody Blues*

Paint it Black. . . . . *The Rolling Stones*

Pink Cadillac. . . . .*Natalie Cole*

Pretty in Pink. . . . .*Psychedelic Furs*

Purple People Eater. . . . .*Jackie Dennis*

Purple Haze. . . . .*Jimi Hendrix*

Purple Rain. . . . . *Prince*

Raspberry Beret. . . . . *Prince*

Red Alert. . . . .*Basement Jaxx*

Red Light, Green Light. . . . .*Mitchell Torok*

Red Light Spells Danger. . . . . *Billy Ocean*

Red River Rock. . . . . *Johnny and the Hurricanes*

Rudolph the Red Nose Reindeer. . . . .*Traditional*

singing the blues

Silver Star. . . . .*The Four Seasons*

Silver Machine. . . . .*Hawkwind*

Silver Dream Machine. . . . . *David Essex*

Singin' the Blues. . . . . *Guy Mitchell*

Song Sung Blue. . . . .*Neil Diamond*

That Old Black Magic. . . . . *Sammy Davis Jr*

Tie a Yellow Ribbon. . . . . *Dawn*

White Christmas. . . . .*Bing Crosby*

White Flag. . . . .*Dido*

White Horses. . . . . *Jackie Lee*

White Wedding. . . . .*Billy Idol*

Whiter Shade of Pale. . . . .*Procul Harem*

Yellow. . . . .*Coldplay*

Yellow River. . . . .*Christie*

Yellow Rose of Texas. . . . . *Mitch Miller*

simple simon

This category contains well known people whose first names and surnames begin with the same letter. For the purposes of this game 'well known' means recognised by a majority of the people playing the game.

Our list includes both real people and fictitious characters but you can decide what is acceptable. There are names for nearly every letter so it is a good one to do alphabetically.

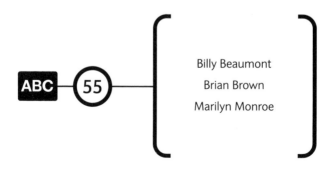

ABC 55

Billy Beaumont
Brian Brown
Marilyn Monroe

simple simon

Alan Alda	Kris Kristopherson
Arthur Ashe	Linda Lusardi
Boris Becker	Linda Lewis
Brian Blessed	Lucy Liu
Bridget Bardot	Magnus Magnusson
Billy Brag	Michael Myers
Christopher Columbus	Michael Moore
Chevy Chase	Martine McCutcheon
Colin Chapman	Nick Nolte
Dan Dare	Olive Oil
Dickie Davies	Peter Powell
David Dimbleby	Peter Pan
Doris Day	Peter Parker (Spiderman)
Edna Everidge	Peter Purves
Frederick Forsythe	Phil Parkes
Frank Finlay	Robert Redford
Fred Funk	Ronald Regan
George Graham	Roy Rogers
Graham Greene	Richard Rogers
Graham Gooch	Sharon Stone
Harry Hill	Susan Sarandon
Holly Hunter	Sylvester Stallone
Jack Jones	Tommy Trinder
Jesse James	Terry Thomas
Jilly Johnson	Tina Turner
Kevin Kline	Wilber Wright

commercial break

Nowadays there seems to be more adverts than programmes on tv, but just how many advertising slogans can you remember?

A great game for recalling some of those classic adverts from the past, but, make sure people are accurate with the slogans and know the correct name of the product or brand. Where the slogans are very long we have just given you a start.

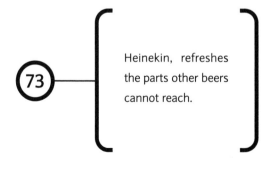

(73) Heinekin, refreshes the parts other beers cannot reach.

commercial break

The fourth emergency service . . . . *The AA*

Just AAsk. . . . . *AA Insurance*

Get the Abbey habit . . . . *Abbey National*

Your flexible friend . . . . *Access*

Don't leave home without it . . . . *American Express*

Think different . . . . *Apple Computers*

Vorsprung durch technik . . . . *Audi*

I'd love a Babycham . . . . *Babycham*

Sweet as the moment when the pod went pop. . . . . *Birds Eye*

Aah Bisto. . . . . *Bisto*

The ultimate driving machine . . . . *BMW*

A taste of paradise. . . . . *Bounty*

The world's favourite airline . . . . *British Airways*

Splash it all over . . . . *Brut*

It's good to talk . . . . *BT*

The king of beers . . . . *Budweiser*

Have you got the urge?. . . . . *Burger King*

A glass and a half in every pound . . . . *Cadbury's Dairy Milk*

Roses grow on you . . . . *Cadbury's Roses*

Probably the best lager in the world . . . . *Carlsberg*

Australians wouldn't give a XXXX . . . . *Castlemaine*

The real thing . . . . *Coca Cola*

The man from Delmonte he say "yes". . . . . *Delmonte*

What's the worst that can happen? . . . . *Dr Pepper*

Hand built by robots . . . . *Fiat Strada*

No FT no comment . . . . *Financial Times*

They're GRRRRReat. . . . .*Frosties*

Full of Eastern promise. . . . . *Frys Turkish Delight*

The best a man can get. . . . .*Gillette*

Pure genius . . . .*Guinness*

Don't be vague, ask for Haig . . . . *Haig Whisky*

Happiness is a cigar called . . . .*Hamlet*

Refreshes the parts other beers cannot reach . . . .*Heineken*

Beanz meanz Heinz . . . .*Heinz Baked Beans*

Follow the bear. . . . .*Hoffmeister Lager*

Don't say brown say Hovis . . . .*Hovis*

It is. Are you? . . . .*The Independent*

Say it with flowers . . . . *Interflora*

Have a break have a. . . . .*Kit Kat*

You can't get quicker than a Kwikfit fitter. . . . . *Kwikfit*

Because you're worth It . . . .*Loreal*

A Mars a day helps you work, rest and play. . . . .*Mars*

Anytime, any place, anywhere . . . .*Martini*

Maybe she's born with it, maybe it's. . . . .*Maybelline*

I'm lovin it. . . . .*McDonalds*

All because the lady loves . . . .*Milk Tray*

It could be you. . . . .*National Lottery*

Just do it . . . . *Nike*

Made to make your mouth water. . . . . *Opal Fruits*

The future's bright, the future's. . . . .*Orange*

Top breeders recommend it. . . . . *Pedigree Chum*

P P P Pick up a Penguin . . . . *Penguin Biscuits*

commercial break

Lipsmakin' thirstquenchin' acetastin' motivatin' . . . . . . *Pepsi*

It's a lot less bovver than a hover. . . . .*Qualcast Mower*

I liked it so much I bought the company. . . . . . . *Remington*

Snap, crackle and pop . . . .*Rice Crispies*

Schhh, you know who. . . . . *Schweppes*

You can be sure of. . . . . *Shell*

For mash get Smash. . . . .*Smash*

Reassuringly expensive. *Stella Artois*

You know when you've been tangoed . . . .*Tango*

Every little helps. . . . .*Tesco*

Don't just book it, Thomas Cook it . . . .*Thomas Cook*

Hello tosh gotta Toshiba. . . . .*Toshiba*

The car in front is a. . . . .*Toyota*

The bank that likes to say yes. . . . .*TSB*

Typhoo puts the T in Britain . . . .*Typhoo* Tea

If only everything in life was as reliable as. . . . . *Volkswagen*

Hello boys . . . .*Wonder bra*

We're with the Woolwich . . . . . . *Woolwich Building Society*

Let your fingers do the walking. . . . .*Yellow Pages*

The appliance of science. . . . . *Zanussi*

noah's ark

A straight forward list of animals, sounds easy doesn't it? However, this is a game you must play alphabetically. There is only one letter we haven't found an answer for and although a few of the animals listed are rare, most will be known by everyone.

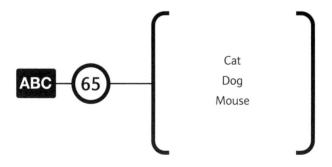

ABC 65
[
Cat
Dog
Mouse
]

noah's ark

Aadvark	Hyena	Tiger
Armadillo	Ibex	Turtle
Ass	Impala	Tapir
Badger	Jaguar	Vole
Bear	Jackal	Water Rat
Boar	Kangaroo	Wildebeast
Buffalo	Koala Bear	Wolf
Beaver	Leopard	Xantus
Camel	Lion	Yak
Chimpanzee	Lynx	Zebra
Chipmunk	Mandrill	
Cow	Moose	
Deer	Monkey	
Elephant	Newt	
Elk	Otter	
Ferret	Orang Utan	
Fox	Panther	
Giraffe	Pig	
Goat	Quokka	
Gorilla	Rabbit	
Guinea Pig	Rat	
Goose	Reindeer	
Hedgehog	Rhinocerous	
Hare	Sheep	
Hippopotamus	Sloth	
Horse	Squirrel	

name names

Well known people who have a last name that is also a first name. As usual 'well known' means recognised by a majority of the people playing the game, and, if there is any doubt as to whether a particular surname can genuinely be used as a first name, the person answering must come up with an example of a well known person using that name.

Sounds complicated, doesn't it? But the examples below should give you a good idea of what you are looking for.

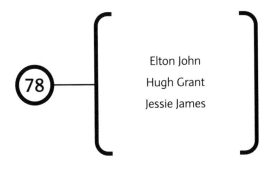

78

Elton John
Hugh Grant
Jessie James

name names

Adam Faith
Anne Frank
Barry John
Barry Norman
Ben Elton
Bill Owen
Billy Graham
Billy Paul
Bea Arthur
Bo Derek
Bruce Lee
Buddy Holly
Carly Simon
Charlie George
Chuck Norris
Craig Charles
Cliff Richard
Craig David
Crystal Gale
Darryl Hannah
Danny Kaye
David Jason
Denholm Elliot
Dennis Willy
Dick Francis
Eddie Grant

Edmund Hilary
Gene Vincent
George Harrison
George Michael
Grace Kelly
Hannah Gordon
Jack Benny
James Dean
Janice Ian
Jim Dale
Kirk Douglas
Jamie Oliver
Jane Russell
Jason Donovan
Jim Clarke
Jimmy Cliff
John Glenn
Jonathon Ross
Johnny Morris
Josie Lawrence
Kurt Russell
Lenny Bruce
Lenny Henry
Les Dennis
Leslie Joseph
Lewis Carroll

Laura Ashley
Matt Damon
Meg Ryan
Michael Douglas
Nelson Eddie
Nigel Benn
Paul Nicholas
Paul Simon
Penelope Keith
Peter Gabriel
Peter Kay
Ray Charles
Rob Andrew
Robert Lindsay
Rod Stewart
Russell Grant
Sam Neill
Shane Ritchie
Sid James
Spencer Tracey
Wendy Craig
Wendy Richard
Woody Allen

car heaven

A great trip down memory lane although not in one of these, at least not a new one. The criteria for this section is cars that are no longer in production.

We have limited the answers to cars commonly available in this country and have kept the list simple by including names only and avoiding any number references like 1100, 2000TDi, 1600i, etc etc, however the choice is yours.

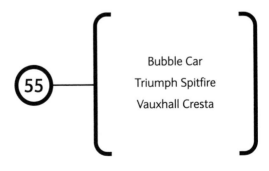

55

Bubble Car
Triumph Spitfire
Vauxhall Cresta

car heaven

Austin Allegro	Jenson Interceptor
Austin Cambridge	Lancia Beta
Austin Maestro	Lancia Delta
Austin Maxi	Lotus Elan
Austin Metro	Lotus Elite
Austin Montego	MGB GT
Austin Westminster	MG Midget
Austin Healy Sprite	Morris Marina
Bond Bug	Morris Minor
Citreon Diane	Morris Oxford
Daimler Majestic	Reliant Robin
Ford Anglia	Reliant Scimiter
Ford Capri	Singer Vouge
Ford Consul	Sunbeam Alpine
Ford Corsair	Sunbeam Rapier
Ford Cortina	Sunbeam Talbot
Ford Escort	Triumph Dolomite
Ford Granada	Triumph Herald
Ford Zephyr	Triumph Mayflower
Ford Zodiac	Triumph Stag
Hillman Imp	Triumph Toledo
Hillman Hunter	Triumph Vittesse
Hillman Husky	Vauxhall Viva
Humber Snipe	Vauxhall Victor
Jaguar E Type	Vauxhall Velox
Jaguar XJS	Wolsey Hornet

place names

Some people are born to lead and some people are born in Peckham but, wherever they come from, all these well known people have places in their names and have put themselves on the map in more ways than one.

You should reward creative thinking in this section so any answers that get a laugh or sound like a place without perhaps being spelt correctly are perfectly acceptable.

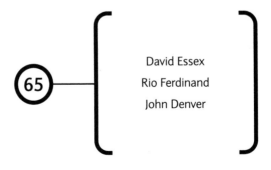

65

David Essex
Rio Ferdinand
John Denver

place names

Brooklyn Beckham	Patricia Hayes	Billy Preston
Alan Brazil	Don Henley	Angela Rippon
Irving Berlin	Charlton Heston	Diana Ross
Johnny Bristol	Jules Holland	Jonathan Ross
Michael Bolton	Rod Hull	Johnny Vegas
Richard Burton	Whitney Huston	Dionne Warwick
Belinda Carlisle	Jill Ireland	Denzil Washington
Charlie Chester	Jordan	Barry White
Chelsea Clinton	Felicity Kendal	Barbara Windsor
Jimmy Clitheroe	Sarah Lancashire	Susannah York
Bing Crosby	Burt Lancaster	
Windsor Davies	Mike Lee	
Jack Dee	Vivian Leigh	
Kirk Douglas	Mark Lester	
Terence Trent Derby	Abraham Lincoln	
Justin Edinburgh	Jack London	
Harry Enfield	Devon Malcolm	
Mike England	Jane Mansfield	
Colin Firth	Somerset Maughn	
James Galway	Paul Merton	
William Hague	Dudley Moore	
Susan Hampshire	Eric Morecambe	
Jean Harlow	Florence Nightingale	
Asa Hartford	Simon Mayo	
Gavin Hastings	Mica Paris	
Isaac Hayes	River Pheonix	

pearls of wisdom

What is a pearl of wisdom in the context of the game? We would define it as a well known phrase that contains some undeniable truth.

This is a big section and a good one to do alphabetically, we found only four letters, including X & Z that we couldn't think of at least one answer for - perhaps you can do better.

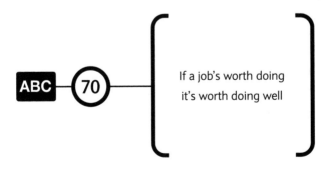

ABC (70)

If a job's worth doing
it's worth doing well

pearls of wisdom

A stitch in time saves nine

All good things must come to an end

All's well that ends well

All's fair in love and war

Beauty is only skin deep

Beggars can't be choosers

Better late than never

Better to be safe than sorry

Better the devil you know

Birds of a feather flock together

Blood is thicker than water

Charity begins at home

Cleanliness is next to godliness

Curiosity killed the cat

Don't count your chickens before they're hatched

Don't put off 'til tomorrow what you can do today

Discretion is the better part of valour

Don't put all your eggs in one basket

Don't cut off your nose to spite your face

Easy come, easy go

Every dog has his day

Every picture tells a story

Every cloud has a silver lining

Familiarity breeds contempt

Fools rush in where angels fear to tread

Great minds think alike

He who hesitates is lost

He who dares wins

Ignorance is bliss

In for a penny, in for a pound

It's no use crying over spilt milk

It takes two to tango

Jack of all trades, master of none

Let sleeping dogs lie

Lightning never strikes twice

Look before you leap

Make hay while the sun shines

Many hands make light work

Money is the root of all evil

Necessity is the mother of invention

Never look a gift horse in the mouth

Nothing ventured, nothing gained

No news is good news

One good turn deserves another

Patience is a virtue

People who live in glass houses shouldn't throw stones

Practice what you preach

Revenge is sweet

Robbing Peter to pay Paul

Silence is golden

Spare the rod and spoil the child

Still waters run deep

pearls of wisdom

The best things in life are free
The bigger they are the harder they fall
The early bird catches the worm
The grass is always greener on the other side
The proof of the pudding is in the eating
There is more than one way to skin a cat
There's no fool like an old fool
There's no place like home
There's no smoke without fire
Too many cooks spoil the broth
United we stand, divided we fall
Variety is the spice of life
Virtue is its own reward
Waste not want not
Where there's a will there's a way
You can't make an omelette without breaking eggs
You win some, you lose some

background music

Often the unsung heroes behind the famous names, this category is all about backing groups.

To avoid arguments we have only included groups that can be preceded by the words 'and the' so bands like Herman's Hermits & Dexy's Midnight Runners are not included. Make sure you get the lead singer and the backing group for a correct answer.

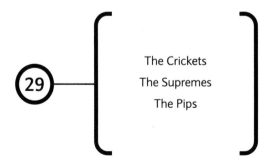

29 — The Crickets
The Supremes
The Pips

background music

The Ants . . . .*Adam*

The Attractions . . . . *Elvis Costello*

The Blue Flames . . . .*Georgie Fame*

The Blackhearts . . . .*Joan Jett*

The Blockheads . . . .*Ian Dury*

The Bluenotes. . . . .*Harold Melvin*

The Bunnymen . . . .*Echo*

The Coconuts . . . . *Kid Creole*

The Comets . . . .*Bill Haley*

The Dakotas . . . .*Billy J Kramer*

The Dreamers . . . .*Freddy*

The E Street Band . . . .*Bruce Springsteen*

The Family Stone . . . .*Sly*

The First Edition . . . . *Kenny Rogers*

The Four Seasons . . . . *Frankie Valli*

The Gang . . . .*Kool*

The Heartbreakers . . . . *Tom Petty*

The Mindbenders . . . . *Wayne Fontana*

The Miracles. . . . . *Smokey Robinson*

The MGs. . . . . *Booker T*

The Pacemakers. . . . .*Gerry*

The Shadows. . . . . *Cliff Richard*

The Silver Bullet Band. . . . .*Bob Seger*

The Sunshine Band. . . . .*KC*

The Vandellas. . . . .*Martha Reeves*

The Wailers. . . . .*Bob Marley*

take two

However many takes they took the films in this category all have a number in their title. As well as numbers you can also include first, second, third, etc, and for the film buffs among you, you could make the game harder by going up in numerical order.

There are quite a few to choose from, we've listed over 50 but who's counting? Oh yes, sorry, you are!

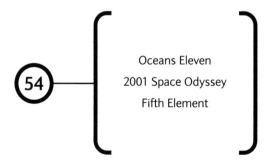

One Flew Over the Cuckoo's Nest

One Fine Day

Two Mules for Sister Sarah

The Man with Two Brains

Three Kings

3 Men and a Baby

The Three Musketeers

The Third Man

Close Encounters of the 3rd Kind

Four Weddings and a Funeral

The Four Seasons

Five Easy Pieces

Six Degrees of Separation

Sixth Sense

Seven

Magnificent Seven

The Seven Samurai

Seven Brides for Seven Brothers

Seven Year Itch

Butterfield 8

8 Mile

Eight Men Out

Nine to Five

Nine and a Half Weeks

10

The Ten Commandments

Ten Things I Hate About You

Force 10 From Navarone

10 Rillington Place

The Dirty Dozen

12 Monkeys

Twelve Angry Men

Friday the 13th

Assault on Precinct 13

Appollo 13

Miracle of 34th Street

Thirty Nine Steps

42nd Street

48 Hours

50 First Dates

The 51st State

55 Days at Peking

Airport 77

84 Charing Cross Road

101 Dalmations

Fahrenheit 451

633 Squadron

1984

20000 Leagues Under The Sea

Brewster's Millions

Billion Dollar Brain

r.i.p. tv

Gone but not forgotten, at least you hope so when you play this game. The ultimate nightmare for a soap star, to be written out of the series. The people in this category are all deceased characters from current soaps. We have included Eastenders, Coronation Street, Emmerdale, Neighbours and Hollyoaks, but of course there are plenty of others if you can remember them.

If you are playing with a bunch of soap addicts you might want to include both the character and how they met their maker in the answer.

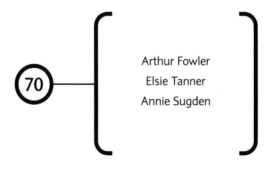

70

Arthur Fowler
Elsie Tanner
Annie Sugden

r.i.p. tv

EASTENDERS

Lou Beale . . . .*Old age*

Pete Beale . . . . *Car accident*

Ashley Cotton . . . .*Motorbike accident*

Charlie Cotton . . . .*Lorry crash*

Ethel Skinner . . . .*Euthanasia*

Jamie Mitchell . . . .*Run over by Martin Fowler*

Barry Evans . . . . . . *Fell down a cliff and left to die by Janine*

Roy Evans . . . .*Heart attack*

Steve Owen . . . . *Blown up in car*

Trevor Morgan . . . . *Went up in flames*

Angie Watts . . . .*Kidney failure*

Saskia Duncan . . . . *Murdered by Steve Owen*

Tiffany Mitchell . . . . *Run over by Frank*

Tom Banks . . . .*Died in fire trying to save Trevor*

Eddie Royle . . . .*Stabbed by Nick Cotton*

CORONATION STREET

Richard Hillman . . . .*Drove into canal*

Duggie Ferguson . *Fell and left for dead by Richard Hillman*

Patricia Hillman . . . .*Hit with spade by Richard Hillman*

Alma Halliwell . . . .*Cancer*

Susan Barlow . . . .*Car crash*

Dean Sykes . . . . *Shot by police in supermarket hold up*

Jez Quigley . . . . *Punctured lung*

Alison Webster . . . .*Run down by a lorry*

Judy Mallet . . . .*Blood clot*

Alf Roberts . . . .*Natural causes*

Des Barnes . . . .*Attacked by drug dealers*

Anne Malone . . . .*Frozen to death in supermarket freezer*

Don Brennan . . . .*Suicide car crash*

Derek Wilton . . . . . .*Heart attack during a road rage incident*

Samir Rachid . . . .*Beaten up*

Brian Tilsley . . . .*Stabbed outside nightclub*

Dennis Stringer . . . . *Car crash rushing Les to hospital*

Alan Bradley . . . . *Knocked down by a tram in Blackpool*

EMMERDALE

Tricia Dingle . . . . *Roof collapse in Woolpack*

Chris Tate . . . . *Suicide*

Ray Mullen . . . .*Pushed down stairs by Louise*

Angie Reynolds . . . .*Killed in car chase*

Sarah Sugden . . . .*Barn fire started by her adopted son*

Butch Dingle . . . . *Bus crash*

Graham Clark . . . .*Car drove over cliff*

Liam Hammond . . . . *Shot by Zoe in kidnapping*

Vic Windsor . . . . *Killed in post office raid*

Frank Tate . . . .*Heart attack while Kim watched him die*

David Glover . . . .*Rescuing baby from fire*

Joe Sugden . . . .*Car crash in Spain*

Henry Wilks . . . .*Heart attack*

r.i.p. tv

NEIGHBOURS

Dee Bliss . . . .*Car drove over cliff into sea*

Drew Kirk . . . .*Fell off horse*

Madge Bishop . . . . *Died from septacemia*

Helen Daniels . . . .*Died in her sleep*

Cheryl Stark . . . .*Hit by a car*

Cody Willis . . . .*Shot by stray bullet from drug dealers*

Julie Martin . . . . *Drunken fall down stairs*

Jim Robinson . . . .*Heart attack*

Todd Landers . . . .*Heart attack after being hit by car*

HOLLYOAKS

Dawn Cunningham . . . .*Died of Leukaemia*

Lewis Richardson . . . .*Overdose*

Jill Patrick . . . . *Brain tumour*

Gordon Cunningham . . . .*Heart attack after car crash*

Helen Cunningham . . . . *Car accident*

Jamie Nash . . . . *Van went over cliff*

Kurt Benson . . . . *Killed in jet ski accident*

Natasha Anderson . . . .*Drug slipped into her drink*

Ollie Benson . . . . *Car accident with Stan*

Stan . . . . *Car accident with Ollie*

Rob Hawthorne . . . .*Died in fire he started*

Toby Mills . . . . *Killed by Dan Hunter*

fruit and veg

With all the familiar favourites and the more exotic items that can be found on the shelves today this is a really long shopping list so there is plenty to choose from.

This section is a really good one to play alphabetically as there are only three letters without answers and one of those is X. But a word of advice, don't play this category with a greengrocer!

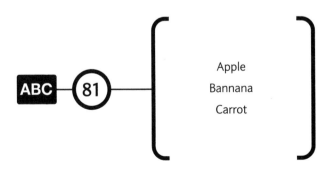

ABC – 81

Apple
Bannana
Carrot

fruit and veg

Artichoke	Fig	Pimento
Asparagus	Gooseberry	Plum
Aubergine	Green pepper	Potato
Avocado	Horseradish	Pumpkin
Beetroot	Juniper	Quince
Broad bean	Jerusalem artichoke	Radicchio
Brussell sprout	Kale	Red pepper
Butter bean	Kholrabi	Rhubarb
Broccoli	Kumquat	Runner bean
Cabbage	Leek	Radish
Cauliflower	Lemon	Raspberry
Celeriac	Lentil	Shallot
Celery	Lime	Spinach
Chard	Mangetout	Squash
Cherry	Marrow	Strawberry
Chicory	Melon	Swede
Chickpea	Mushroom	Sweetcorn
Courgette	Nectarine	Sweet potato
Cranberry	Okra	Strawberry
Cucumber	Onion	Tomato
Damson	Orange	Turnip
Date	Pak choy	Ugli fruit
Eggplant	Parsnip	Watercress
Endive	Peach	Watermelon
Elderberry	Pea	Yam
Fennel	Pepper	Zuchinni

top shops

Top shops in this category must be major stores or retail chains, not small one-shop wonders. There will, of course, be some regional differences and you will have to decide what is acceptable for your area. If you are unsure of an answer, put it to the vote.

Another good category to do alphabetically as the only letters missing are X, Y and Z, unless you know differently.

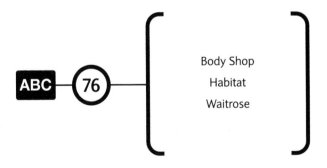

ABC — 76

Body Shop
Habitat
Waitrose

top shops

Alldays	H&M Hennes	Orange
Asda	HMV	PC World
Argos	Homebase	Principles
Accessorize	Hobbycraft	Primark
Boots	Iceland	QS
BHS	John Lewis	River Island
B&Q	JD Sports	Sainsbury
Burtons	John Menzies	Safeway
Clintons	Jessops	Somerfield
Currys	Kookai	Superdrug
Comet	Kwiksave	Tesco
Clarkes	Kallkwik	Threshers
Co-op	Laura Ashley	Top Shop
Dolcis	Littlewoods	Tower Records
Debenhams	Lewis's	Toys R Us
Dixons	MFI	Unwins
Dorothy Perkins	Marks and Spencer	Victoria Wine
Ernest Jones	Matalan	Vodaphone
Evans	Monsoon	Waterstones
Fourboys	Morrisons	WH Smith
Fcuk	Mothercare	Woolworths
Gap	MVC	
Game	Netto	
Greggs	New Look	
H Samuels	Next	
Halfords	Oasis	

sick as a parrot

Don't stand too close to each other when you play this game as it might be contagious. Not one for the faint hearted but hypochondriacs could play their joker on it. How many illnesses can you think of?

If there is any doubt about any of the answers make sure people can describe the symptoms. As with all the categories a clever answer can be as good as a correct answer.

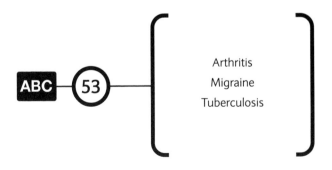

ABC — 53

Arthritis
Migraine
Tuberculosis

sick as a parrot

Aids

Alzheimers

Anaemia

Asthma

Bubonic plague

Bulimia

Bronchitis

Cancer

Chickenpox

Cholera

Common Cold

Conjunctivitis

Croup

Diarrhoea

Diabetes

Dysentery

Eczema

Emphacema

Fever

Flu

Gastroenteritis

Gout

Gonorrhoea

Hay Fever

Hives

Influenza

Jaundice

Laryngitis

Malaria

Measles

Meningitis

Mumps

Nausea

Osteoporosis

Parkinsons

Pleurisy

Pneumonia

Polio

Rabies

Rheumatism

Rubella

Shingles

Smallpox

Thrombosis

Tonsillitis

Typhoid

Ulcer

Virus

Whooping cough

Yellow fever

seeing red

One of those categories where you need to think laterally. The answers must be things that are either always red, like blood, traditionally coloured red, like a Ferrari, or where red is an integral part of the answer like The Red Sea.

The answers must be predominantly red and not just have red in them, for instance an Arsenal football shirt is red and white and would not be allowed whereas a Liverpool shirt would be fine.

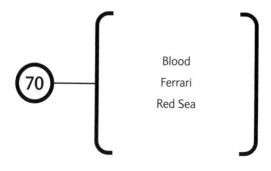

70

Blood
Ferrari
Red Sea

seeing red

Beetroot
Billiard ball
Brake light
Bus lanes
Butlins redcoat
Campari
Cherry
Chinese flag
Cricket ball
Customs lane
Embarrassment
English rose
Fire engine
Fire extinguisher
Holly berry
Letterbox
Little red book
Little red corvette
Liverpool shirt
London bus
Man Utd shirt
Mars
Matador's cape
Poinicetta
Port
Port light

Raspberry
Red Baron
Red beret
Red cabbage
Red carpet
Red Cross
Red Ensign
Red head
Red herring
Red hot
Red letter day
Red light district
Red meat
Redneck
Red pepper
Red rag to a bull
Red Riding Hood
Red snapper
Red Sonja
Red Square
Red squirrel
Red tape
Rhode Island red
Robin's breast
Santa Claus
Sending off card

Ski run
Sky at night
Snooker balls
Strawberry
The Red Devils
The red eye
The Red Shoes
Tomato
Traffic light
Welsh rugby jersey
Welsh dragon
Wine
Monopoly
The Strand
Trafalgar Sq
Fleet Street

sweet tooth

Some of the sweets in this category will take you right back to your childhood and whilst this section is not limited to sweets that are no longer in the shops, they are the ones you are really looking for.

Those of you with good memories could include a description of the packaging, the price of the sweets or even the slogan or song from the advertisements in your answers.

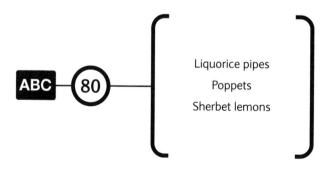

ABC — 80

Liquorice pipes
Poppets
Sherbet lemons

sweet tooth

Aero
Amazin' Raisin Bar
Aniseed Balls
Anglo Bubbly
Aztec
Bar Six
Bulls Eyes
Bandit
Bazooka
Black Jacks
Bounty
Buttons
Caramac
Chocolate Cream
Chocolite
Crunchie
Curly Wurly
Dairy Milk
Dib Dabs
Dolly Mixtures
Drifter
Everton Mints
Fizzels
Flake
Flying Saucers
Fruit Gums

Fruit Pastels
Fruit Salad
Gob Stopper
Gummi Bears
Hubba Bubba
Imperial Mints
Jamboree Bags
Jelly Tots
Kit Kat
Kola Kubes
Lion Bar
Love Hearts
Marathon
Mars Bar
Matchmakers
Melody Pops
Minstrels
Milky Bar
Milky Way
Mint Cracknel
Murray Mints
Nutty Bar
Old Jamaica
Opal Fruits
Pacers
Parma Violets

Pez
Picnic
Pink Panther Bar
Polos
Raider
Refreshers
Revels
Rolos
Roses
Space Dust
Spangles
Spanish Gold
Sherbet Fountains
Sweet Prawns
Skybar
Texan
Toblerone
Toffos
Toffee Crisp
Tooty Frooties
Trebor Mints
Treets
Turkish Delight
Wagon Wheel
Yorkie

me and my shadow

There are a lot of comedy duos in this category but also plenty of room for other double acts. Think composers, singers, cops etc.

The pairings can be fictitious like Starsky and Hutch and can also be cartoon characters like Tom and Jerry but they must all be recognised and inseparable double acts.

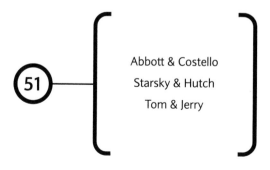

51

Abbott & Costello
Starsky & Hutch
Tom & Jerry

me and my shadow

Morecambe and Wise

The Two Ronnies

Cagney and Lacey

Daziel and Pascoe

Laurel and Hardy

Little and Large

Smith and Jones

Reeves and Mortimer

Hale and Pace

Fry and Laurie

Cannon and Ball

Hinge and Bracket

Pen and Teller

Chas and Dave

Skinner and Baddiel

Ant and Dec

Trev and Simon

Peters and Lee

Mike and Bernie Winters

French and Saunders

Peter Cook and Dudley Moore

Cheech and Chong

Fred Astaire and Ginger Rogers

Bill and Ben

Mork and Mindy

Pinky and Perky

Hall and Oates

Rogers and Hammerstein

Wallace and Grommet

Lennon and McCartney

Torvill and Dean

Sooty and Sweep

Siegfried and Roy

Rowan and Martin

Mulder and Scully

Jeeves and Wooster

Rod Hull and Emu

Gilbert and Sullivan

Barnum and Bailey

Batman and Robin

Flannagan and Allen

Richard and Judy

Smith and Wesson

Ben and Jerry

Bonnie and Clyde

Sapphire and Steele

Anthony and Cleopatra

Bill and Ted

claptrap

Words that rhyme with themselves. At first this seems a very difficult section but as you can see we came up with over forty answers.

The words can be hyphenated but two separate rhyming words like 'go slow' are not acceptable, unless, of course, you are really struggling for answers.

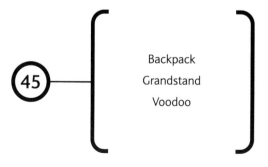

(45)

Backpack
Grandstand
Voodoo

Backtrack

Bandstand

Bedstead

Bigwig

Blackjack

Booboo

Claptrap

Cookbook

Deadhead

Downtown

Fourscore

Handstand

Heyday

Hi-fi

Hobo

Ho-ho

Hoity-toity

Hotpot

Hotshot

Hubbub

Humdrum

Hurly-burly

Kiwi

Loco

Logo

Maintain

Mayday

Nitwit

Oboe

Pay-day

Picnic

Pogo

Polo

Pot-shot

Redhead

Solo

Teepee

Tom-tom

Waylay

Willy-nilly

Yoo-hoo

Yo-yo

working titles

Some people were born to be king, well Stephen was anyway, but for some reason he decided to be an author instead. This category is full of people whose names suggest that they missed their vocation.

You should only include real people in your answers unless you are struggling but don't worry too much if the spelling of the surname is incorrect, as long as it sounds like a job title it is perfectly acceptable.

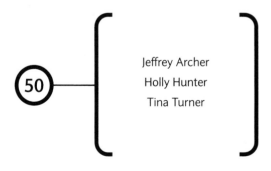

50 {
Jeffrey Archer
Holly Hunter
Tina Turner
}

working titles

Russ Abbot

Danny Baker

Cheryl Baker

Ronnie Barker

Keith Baron

Karen Carpenter

Raymond Chandler

Kenneth Clark

Peter Cook

Sue Cook

Henry Cooper

Norman Collier

Letitia Dean

Minnie Driver

Lord Falconer

Carrie Fisher

Jessica Fletcher

George Foreman

Phillipa Forrester

Ava Gardner

Billy Jean King

Stephen King

Jack Lord

John McVicar

Malcolm Marshall

James Mason

Glen Miller

Arthur Miller

Elaine Page

Nigel Planer

Nyree Dawn Porter

Dennis Potter

Christopher Plummer

Victoria Principal

David Seaman

John Seargant

Cybil Shepherd

Christian Slater

Mel Smith

Elsie Tanner

Elizabeth Taylor

Margaret Thatcher

Lana Turner

Bonny Tyler

Dennis Waterman

Dennis Weaver

Sigourney Weaver

come on down!

No, we are not looking for catchprases, although you could include them in your answers, we are looking for names of tv game shows.

We have also included hosts, as they are often as famous as the shows, so you may want people to get both for a correct answer. Where a show has been hosted by a number of different people we have only named one or two, but you can fill in the gaps.

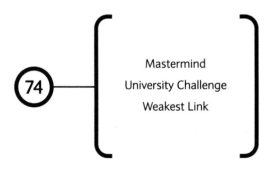

74

Mastermind
University Challenge
Weakest Link

come on down

Ask the Family. . . . . *Robert Robinson/Alan Titchmarsh*

Big Break. . . . . *Jim Davidson*

Blankety Blank. . . . . *Terry Wogan /Les Dawson/Lily Savage*

Blockbusters. . . . .*Bob Holness*

Bob's Full House . . . .*Bob Monkhouse*

Bullseye. . . . . *Jim Bowen*

Busman's Holiday. . . . . *Julian Pettifer/Sarah Kennedy*

Call My Bluff. . . . . *Robin Ray/Robert Robinson*

Catchphrase. . . . . *Roy Walker/Nick Weir/Mark Curry*

Celebrity Squares . . . .*Bob Monkhouse*

Child's Play . . . .*Michael Aspel*

Cluedo . . . .*Various*

Countdown . . . . *Richard Whiteley & Carol Vorderman*

Crystal Maze . . . . *Richard O'Brien/Edward Tudor Pole*

Cross Wits. . . . .*Tom O'Connor*

Dog Eat Dog . . . .*Ulrika Jonsson*

Don't Forget Your Toothbrush . . . .*Chris Evans*

Double Your Money . . . .*Hughie Green*

Every Second Counts . . . .*Paul Daniels*

Face The Music . . . .*Joseph Cooper*

Family Fortunes . . . .*Bob Monkhouse/Les Dennis*

Fifteen To One . . . .*William Stewart*

Friends Like These . . . .*Ant & Dec/Ian Wright*

Generation Game . . . .*Bruce Forsythe/Larry Grayson*

Give Us a Clue . . . . *Michael Aspel/Michael Parkinson*

Going For a Song . . . .*Michael Aspel*

Going For Gold . . . . *Henry Kelly*

Golden Shot . . . .*Bob Monkhouse/Norman Vaughan*

Have I Got News For You . . . . *Angus Deayton*

It's a Knock Out . . . .*David Vine/Stuart Hall*

It's Only TV - But I Like It . . . .*Jonathan Ross*

Krypton Factor . . . . *Gordon Burns*

Mastermind . . . .*Magnus Magnusson*

Mr & Mrs . . . . *Alan Taylor/Derek Batley/Julian Clarey*

Never Mind the Buzzcocks . . . .*Mark Lamarr*

Odd One Out . . . .*Paul Daniels*

Pass The Buck . . . .*Fred Dinenage/Eamonn Holmes*

Pets Win Prizes . . . . *Danny Baker/Dale Winton*

Play Your Cards Right . . . .*Bruce Forsythe*

Pop Quest . . . .*Kid Jensen /Sally James*

Pop Quiz . . . .*Mike Reid*

Punchlines . . . . *Lennie Bennet*

Question of Sport . .*David Vine/David Coleman/Sue Barker*

Quizball . . . . *David Vine/Barry Davies/Stuart Hall*

Runaround . . . .*Mike Reid/Leslie Crowther/Stan Boardman*

Sale Of The Century . . . .*Nicholas Parsons*

Screen Test . . . . *Michael Rodd/Brian Trueman/Mark Curry*

Shooting Stars . . . .*Vic Reeves & Bob Mortimer*

Spot The Tune . . . .*Ted Ray/Pete Murray*

Strike It Rich. . . . . *Michael Barrymore*

Supermarket Sweep . . . .*Dale Winton*

Take Your Pick . . . . *Michael Miles/Des O'Connor*

come on down

Tele Addicts . . . . *Noel Edmonds*

The Chair . . . . *John McEnroe*

The Main Event. . . . . *Chris Tarrant*

The Moment Of Truth . . . . *Cilla Black*

The Price is Right . . . . *Leslie Crowther/Bruce Forsythe*

The Sky's The Limit . . . . *Hughie Green & Monica Rose*

They Think It's All Over . . . . *Nick Hancock*

3-2-1 . . . . *Ted Rogers*

Top Of The Form . . . . *Geoffrey Wheeler*

University Challenge . . .*Bamber Gascoigne/Jeremy Paxman*

Weakest Link . . . . *Anne Robinson*

Wipeout . . . . *Bob Monkhouse*

What's My Line . . . . *Eamon Andrews*

Wheel Of Fortune . . . . *Nicky Campbell*

Who Wants To Be a Millionaire . . . . *Chris Tarrant*

Whodunnit . . . . *Edward Woodward/John Pertwee*

Win Lose Or Draw . . *Danny Baker/Shane Ritchie/Bob Mills*

Winner Takes All . . . . *Jimmy Tarbuck/Geoffrey Wheeler*

You Bet . . . . *Bruce Forsythe/Matthew Kelly*

it's your round

This could be a very expensive round - our list features nearly eighty different alcoholic drinks - how many can you think of? This is a good list to do alphabetically as there are plenty to choose from. We have included both brand names like Archers and drink types like Brandy.

We have left out wine brands and real ale varieties as they often seem to cause an argument as to whether they are genuine or not but the choice is yours.

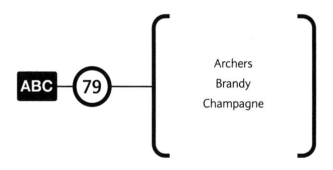

ABC (79)

Archers
Brandy
Champagne

it's your round

Asti Spumante	Gordons	Perrier Jouet
Absolut	Gilbeys	Pinot Grigio
Absinth	Grappa	Pinot Noir
Advocaat	Gin	Port
Armagnac	Grenadine	Ricard
Bacardi	Glenfiddich	Retsina
Bourbon	Glenmorangie	Ruddles
Beer	Guinness	Rum
Baileys	Grolsch	Red Wine
Becks	Harveys	Sherry
Budweiser	John Smiths	Smirnoff
Boddingtons	Jamesons	Sparkling Wine
Cointreau	Jack Daniels	Sambuca
Carling	Kalhua	Southern Comfort
Cognac	Krug	Strongbow
Corona	Lager	Tequilla
Claret	Lowenbrau	Tia Maria
Creme de Menthe	Liebfraumilch	Vodka
Drambuie	Murphys	Vermouth
Dessert wine	Michelob	Whiskey
Dooleys	Miller	Wine
Egg Nog	Merlot	XXXX
Eau de Vie	Malibu	Youngs
Fino	Moet Chandon	Zinfandel
Fosters	Orangeboom	
Frangellico	Pernod	

trains, planes and automobiles

This category includes anything you can ride in or on. We only found two letters for which we couldn't think of at least one answer, so it is a good one to do alphabetically.

Make sure people keep to distinct types of transport like car or plane, brand names like Porsche 911 or Boeing 747 are not acceptable.

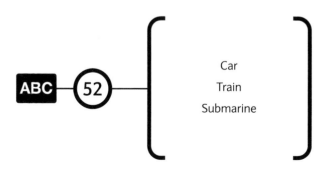

trains, planes and automobiles

Aeroplane

Barge

Bicycle

Bus

Boat

Cable car

Canoe

Catamaran

Chariot

Coach

Dinghy

Dog sled

Donkey

Dragster

Elephant

Flying Boat

GoKart

Helicopter

Horse

Hot air balloon

Jeep

Jet Ski

Kyak

Limousine

Liner

Lorry

Moped

Motorbike

Open Top Bus

Pedalo

Quad Bike

Raft

Rickshaw

Scooter

Sedan

Skiddoo

Sleigh

Snowmobile

Speedboat

Stagecoach

Tank

Taxi

Tractor

Tram

Truck

Unicycle

Van

Wagon

Yacht

child's play

Definitely no computer games allowed in this category and also no grown up games like Trivial Pursuit, but pretty much any other toy or game is acceptable.

Action figures and dolls are ok but only if they are remembered by most of the people playing. The answers must also be specific, so toys like 'a bike' or 'a football' do not count.

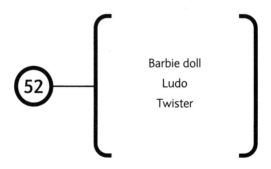

52

Barbie doll
Ludo
Twister

child's play

Action Man
Barrel of Monkeys
Battling Tops
Buccaneer
Buckaroo
Booby Trap
Chess
Cindy Doll
Connect Four
Criss Cross
Cluedo
Draughts
Etch-A-Sketch
Frustration
Fuzzy Felt
Go
Hands Down
Hot Wheels
Johnny Seven Gun
Kerplunk
Klackers
Lego
Meccano
Mine A Million
Monopoly
Mousetrap

Mr Potato Head
Operation
Plasticene
Play Doh
Pick Up Stix
Rat Race
Risk
Rubix Cube
Stratego
Shaker Maker
Six Million Dollar Man
Sketchagraph
Spirograph
Slinky
Snakes & Ladders
Space Hopper
Stretch Armstrong
Subbuteo
Tiny Tears
Tip It
Top Trumps
Uno
Yo-Yo

the green room

How many things can you think of that are coloured green? Although a lot of them will be provided by mother nature, with a little creative thinking, you should be able to think of a few others.

So off you GO! (But only if the light's on green)

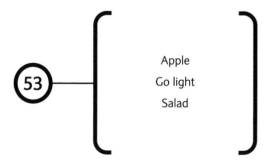

53

Apple
Go light
Salad

the green room

Alligator

Army uniform

Artichoke

Asparagus

Avocado

Berets

Broccoli

Cabbage

Cactus

Caterpillar

Celery

Clover

Cucumber

District Line

Dollar Bill

Dragon

Emerald

Frog

Green Line Bus

Green Mile

Green Jackets

Golf green

Grass

Hedge

Holly

Ivy

Jade

Jealousy

Jolly Green Giant

Kermit the Frog

Leaf

Leprechaun

Lime

Martian

Mint

Mistletoe

Moss

Olive

Parsley

Peas

Pepper

Robin Hood

Shakin' Stevens' door

Starboard light

Table tennis table

Tea

Verdigris

Monopoly

Bond St

Oxford Street

Regent Street

one word wonders

One word bands or solo artistes. The important thing here is to make sure the answers are genuinely one word, for instance Beatles, Jam and Eurythmics are all incorrect because they all have the word 'The' in front of them.

If you get any argument you will just have to put it to the vote and if you haven't heard of a particular band or artiste get the player to sing one of their hits.

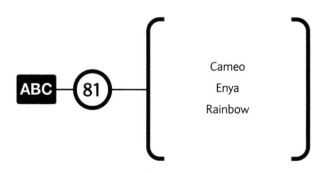

ABC — 81

Cameo
Enya
Rainbow

one word wonders

Abba	Genesis	Rush
Aerosmith	Hawkwind	Sade
America	Hearsay	Santana
Argent	Imagination	Shaggy
Bananarama	Inxs	Showaddywaddy
Bjork	Journey	Slade
Blondie	Junior	Squeeze
Blue	Kajagoogoo	Steps
Blur	Kiss	Stereophonics
Boyzone	Kraftwerk	Sting
Bread	Lindisfarne	Supergrass
Busted	Lulu	Sweet
Cher	Madness	Tatu
Chicago	Madonna	Tavares
Chumbawumba	Meatloaf	Texas
Coldplay	Motorhead	Toploader
Cream	Mud	Travis
Dawn	Nazareth	Ultravox
Dido	Nirvana	Westlife
Donovan	Oasis	Wham
Eminem	Odyssey	Wheatus
Erasure	Pink	Wings
Eternal	Prince	Wizzard
Foreigner	Pulp	Yazoo
Free	Queen	Yazz
Gabrielle	Radiohead	Yes

noun or name

Is it a noun.....is it a name?

It's actually names that are nouns and nouns that are names. Confused? Don't be, just look at the three examples below to see what we mean. All three can be used as a person's name or as an ordinary word.

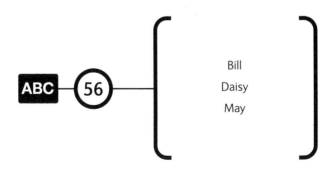

ABC 56

Bill
Daisy
May

noun or name

Amber	Faith	Miles
Ant	Frank	Nick
Basil	Gene	Noel
Beryl	Glen	Olive
Brandy	Grace	Page
Brook	Hank	Pearl
Carol	Heather	Ray
Cat	Holly	Robin
Chandler	Iris	Rose
Crystal	Jack	Ruby
Dale	Jade	Sandy
Dan	Joy	Summer
Dawn	Lance	Teddy
Dean	Laurel	Victor
Derrick	Lily	Violet
Destiny	Mark	Warren
Drew	Mat	Will
Earl	Mike	

tv toons

How many tv cartoon shows can you name?

The answers in our list are all cartoons and not computer graphics or puppets. They have all appeared on UK television as a series and not a one off show or film. This means that Disney films are not allowed.

We have listed the names of the shows rather than the individual cartoon characters, however, what you accept as a correct answer is entirely up to you.

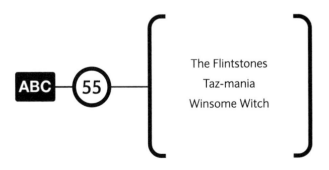

ABC—55

The Flintstones
Taz-mania
Winsome Witch

tv toons

Asterix

Atom Ant

Bagpuss

Beavis and Butthead

Bugs Bunny

Captain Pugwash

Charlie Brown & Snoopy

Crystal Tips & Alistair

Danger Mouse

Deputy Dawg

Earthworm Jim

Felix the Cat

Futurama

Garfield and friends

Gummi Bears

The Hair Bear Bunch

Hong Kong Phooey

Huckleberry Hound

Inch High Private Eye

Ivor The Engine

The Jetsons

Johnny Quest

King of the Hill

Kipper

Looney Toons

Marine Boy

Mr Magoo

Noggin the Nog

The Perils of Penelope Pitstop

Pink Panther

Pixie and Dixie

Quickdraw McGraw

Recess

Ren and Stimpy

Rhubarb and Custard

Road Runner

Rug Rats

Scooby Doo

The Simpsons

Secret Squirrel

South Park

Squiddley Diddley

Stop That Pigeon

Teenage Mutant Ninja Turtles

Tin Tin

Tom & Jerry

Top Cat

Touché Turtle

Undercover Elephant

Wackey Races

X-Men: Evolution

Yogi Bear

name that tune

Thank heaven for little girls.   All these songs have a girl's name in their title. You can decide whether you will accept lyrics that feature a girl's name or if you are keeping to song titles only.

If someone names a song that no one has heard of you should insist on hearing a rendition of at least part of the song before a decision is made.

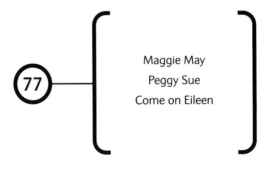

name that tune

Alison . . . . *Elvis Costello*

Angie . . . . *The Rolling Stones*

Annie's Song . . . . *John Denver*

Annie I'm Not Your Daddy . . . . *Kid Creole and the Coconuts*

Barbara Ann . . . . *The Beach Boys*

Black Betty . . . . *Ram Jam*

Billie Jean . . . . *Michael Jackson*

Bette Davis Eyes . . . . *Kim Carnes*

Candida . . . . *Dawn*

Cathy's Clown . . . . *The Everly Brothers*

Carrie Ann . . . . *The Hollies*

Cindy Incidentally . . . . *The Faces*

Claire . . . . *Gilbert O'Sullivan*

Cecilia . . . . *Simon and Garfunkel*

Cracklin' Rose . . . . *Neil Diamond*

Donna *10cc*

Delilah . . . . *Tom Jones*

Eloise . . . . *The Damned*

Eleanor Rigby . . . . *The Beatles*

Emma . . . . *Hot Chocolate*

Gloria . . . . *Van Morrison*

Good Golly Miss Molly . . . . *Little Richard*

Help Me Rhonda . . . . *The Beach Boys*

Hey Jude . . . . *The Beatles*

Hey Paula . . . . *Paul and Paula*

I'm Mandy Fly Me *10cc*

Jean Genie. . . . .*David Bowie*

Jenny From the Block. . . . . *Jennifer Lopez*

Jennifer Juniper. . . . .*Donovan*

Jennifer Eccles. . . . .*The Hollies*

Jolene. . . . .*Dolly Parton*

Joanna. . . . .*Kool and the Gang*

Joan of Ark. . . . . *Orchestral Manoeuvres in the Dark*

Julie Do Ya Love Me. . . . .*White Plains*

Judy Teen. . . . . *Steve Harley and Cockney Rebel*

Judy in Disguise . . . . *John Fred & the Playboy Band*

Lady Eleanor. . . . .*Lindisfarne*

Lady Madonna. . . . . *The Beatles*

Lady Lynda. . . . . *The Beach Boys*

Layla. . . . .*Derek and the Dominoes*

Lola. . . . .*The Kinks*

Lily the Pink. . . . . *The Scaffold*

Lucy in the Sky With Diamonds. . . . . *The Beatles*

Luka. . . . . *Suzanne Vega*

Lucille. . . . .*Little Richard*

Living Next Door to Alice. . . . . *Smokey*

Long Tall Sally. . . . .*Little Richard*

Love Grows Where My Rosemary Goes. .*Edison Lighthouse*

Lovely Rita. . . . . *The Beatles*

Lydia. . . . .*Dean Friedman*

Michelle. . . . . *The Beatles*

Mandy. . . . .*Barry Manilow*

name that tune

Mary of the 4th Form. . . . . *Boomtown Rats*

Marlene on the Wall. . . . .*Suzanne Vega*

Maria. . . . . *Blondie*

Ms Grace. . . . .*The Tymes*

Mustang Sally. . . . . *Wilson Pickett*

Nikita. . . . .*Elton John*

Oh Carolina. . . . .*Shaggy*

Oh Carol. . . . .*Neil Sedaka*

Pictures of Lily. . . . .*The Who*

Poison Ivy. . . . . *The Lambrettas*

Proud Mary. . . . .*Credence Clearwater Revival*

Rhiannon. . . . .*Fleetwood Mac*

Roxanne. . . . . *The Police*

Rosanna. . . . . *Toto*

Ruby Tuesday. . . . .*The Rolling Stones*

Ruby Don't Take Your Love to Town. . . . .*Kenny Rogers*

Run Around Sue. . . . . *Dion*

Sandy. . . . . *John Travolta*

See Emily Play. . . . . *Pink Floyd*

Sylvia's Mother. . . . . *Dr Hook*

Suzanne. . . . . *Leonard Cohen*

Wake Up Little Suzie. . . . .*Buddy Holly*

music to your ears

If you are playing with a group of long haired, bespectacled music buffs then pick another category, but if not there are plenty of music styles here for everyone to choose from.

If you are unsure about any of the answers you are given ask the player to give you a song or artiste associated with the music style in question. Failing that they could always provide a sample of the music itself.

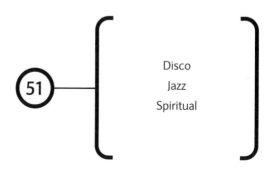

51 {
Disco
Jazz
Spiritual
}

music to your ears

Ambient	Latin
Accapella	Mariachi
Acid House	Merengue
Baroque	New Romantic
Blues	Opera
Boogie Woogie	Pop
Bossa Nova	Progressive
Calypso	Punk
Classical	R&B
Country	Ragtime
Dance	Rap
Dixieland	Reggae
DooWop	Rock
Easy Listening	Rockabilly
Flamenco	Salsa
Folk	Ska
Funk	Skiffle
Garage	Soul
Go Go	Techno
Gospel	Underground
Gregorian Chants	Vaudeville
Heavy Metal	Western
Hip Hop	
House	
Indie	
Industrial	

come fly with me

I'm leaving on a jet plane, but which one. Airlines past and present are what you're looking for and, as with all the categories, you should accept some creative thinking when you start running out of names.

We have included a couple of fictitious airlines in our list and there are bound to be some more.

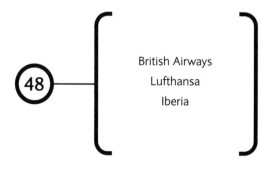

British Airways
Lufthansa
Iberia

come fly with me

Aer Lingus	Icelandair
Aeroflot	JAT
Air 2000	KLM
Air Canada	Korean Air
Air China	Luxair
Air France	Monarch
Air India	Olympic
Alitalia	Pan Am
American	Philippine
BEA	Qantas
BMI	Royal Air Maroc
Britannia	Ryanair
British Caledonian	SAS
British Midlands	Swiss Air
Buzz	TAP
Cathay Pacific	TWA
Coconut Airways	United
Con Air	Varig
Continental	Virgin
Delta	
Easyjet	
Egyptair	
El Al	
Finnair	
Go	
Gulfair	

body talk

Head, shoulders, knees and toes, knees and toes... and of course all the other bits in between. Beware of doctors, nurses and fitness instructors on this one.

When it comes to parts of the body there is a lot to choose from so this is another one of those categories that you must play alphabetically. If people start speaking in Latin make sure they know exactly where the part of the body in their answer can be found.

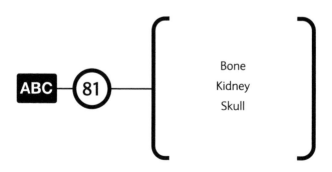

ABC — 81 —

Bone
Kidney
Skull

body talk

Adam's Apple	Fibula	Nail
Abdomen	Foot	Neck
Ankle	Finger	Nerve
Appendix	Forehead	Nose
Arm	Forearm	Oesophagus
Artery	Gall bladder	Pancreas
Bladder	Groin	Quadraceps
Bottom	Gum	Rib
Bowel	Hair	Shin
Brain	Hand	Shoulder
Breast	Head	Skin
Buttocks	Heart	Spine
Calf	Heel	Spleen
Cartilage	Hip	Sternum
Cervix	Instep	Stomach
Cheek	Intestine	Teeth
Chest	Jaw	Tendon
Chin	Knee	Thigh
Clavicle	Larynx	Thumb
Collar bone	Leg	Toe
Colon	Ligament	Tongue
Deltoid	Lips	Trachea
Diaphragm	Liver	Uterus
Ear	Lung	Vein
Elbow	Mouth	Vertebrae
Eye	Muscle	Wrist

have a ball

It doesn't matter what shape or colour they are as long as the game involves balls in this category.

A good game for sportsmen of all ages but always remember, old golfers never die, they only loose their balls.

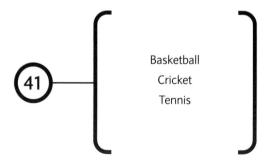

have a ball

Bagatelle	Rugby Union
Baseball	Shinty
Bar Billiards	Skittles
Beach Football	Snooker
Billiards	Softball
Boules	Subbutteo
Bowls	Table Tennis
Bowling	Table Football
Crazy Golf	Shot Putt
Croquet	Squash
Football	Volleyball
Gaelic Football	Water Polo
Golf	
Handball	
Hockey	
Kabaddi	
Lacrosse	
Marbles	
Netball	
Petanque	
Pinball	
Polo	
Pool	
Real Tennis	
Rounders	
Rugby League	

a test of character

A variation on a theme, we have included a number of short lists in one big category. Pick a show and name its fictional characters. There is a whole host of excellent shows to choose from, we have picked a few to start you off, all of which have at least ten memorable characters.

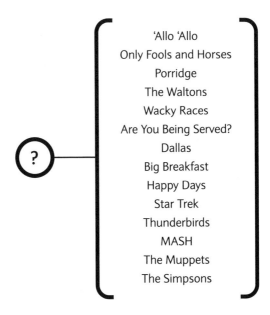

'Allo 'Allo
Only Fools and Horses
Porridge
The Waltons
Wacky Races
Are You Being Served?
Dallas
Big Breakfast
Happy Days
Star Trek
Thunderbirds
MASH
The Muppets
The Simpsons

a test of character

'ALLO 'ALLO

Rene

Edith

Yvette

Maria

Michelle

Col Von Strohm

Capt. Geering

Lt. Gruber

Helga

Herr Flick

M. Leclerc

Mimi

M. Alphonse

Fanny

Flying officer Fairfax

Flying officer Carstairs

Capt. Bertorelli

ONLY FOOLS AND HORSES

Derek 'Del Boy' Trotter

Rodney Trotter

Grandad

Uncle Albert

Raquel

Cassandra

Aubrey 'Boycie' Boyce

Marlene Boyce

Trigger

Mike Fisher

Mickey Pearce

Denzil

Jevon

PORRIDGE

Norman Stanley Fletcher

Lennie Godber

Mr Mackay

Mr Barrowclough

Harry Grout

Lukewarm

Ives

McLaren

Warren

Blanco Webb

Mr Geoffrey Venables

Harris

Cyril Heslop

Judge Stephen Rawley

THE WALTONS

John Walton

Olivia Walton

Zeb (Grandpa) Walton

Esther (Grandma) Walton

John Boy

Mary Ellen

Jason

Erin

Jim Bob

Ben

Elizabeth

Ike Godsey

Corabeth Godsey

Aimee Godsey

Sheriff Bridges

Mamie Baldwin

Emily Baldwin

Yancy Tucker

WACKY RACES

Dick Dastardly & Muttley

The Mean Machine

Peter Perfect

Turbo Terrific

Penelope Pitstop

Compact Pussycat

Luke and Blubber Bear

Arkansas Chugabug

Rufus Ruffcut & Sawtooth

Buzzwagon

The Slag Brothers

The Boulder Mobile

Prof. Pat Pending

Ring a Ding Convert-a-Car

The General & Pte Pinkley

Army Surplus Special

The Red Max

Crimson Haybailer

The Ant Hill Mob

Bulletproof Bomb

The Gruesome Twosome

Creepy Coupe

ARE YOU BEING SERVED?

Mrs Slocombe

Mr Humphries

Capt Peacock

Mr Rumbold

Miss Brahms

Mr Grainger

Mr Lucas

Young Mr Grace

Old Mr Grace

a test of character

DALLAS
John Ross Ewing (JR)
Eleanor Ewing (Miss Ellie)
Bobby Ewing
Pamela Ewing
Lucy Ewing
Sue Ellen Ewing
Ray Krebbs
Cliff Barnes
Willard 'Digger' Barnes
Gary Ewing
Valene Ewing
Jenna Wade

BIG BREAKFAST
Chris Evans
Gaby Roslin
Paula Yates
Bob Geldof
Mark Lamarr
Keith Chegwin
Mark Little
Paul Ross
Richard Orford
Lily Savage
Zoe Ball

Danni Minogue
Sharron Davies
Rick Adams
Vanessa Feltz
Denise Van Outen
Johnny Vaughan
Melanie Sykes
Kelly Brook
Sara Cox
Liza Tarbuck
Richard Bacon
Gail Porter
Paul Tonkinson
Donna Air
Amanda Byram

HAPPY DAYS
Richie Cunningham
Arthur Fonzarelli
Howard Cunningham
Marion Cunningham
Joanie Cunningham
Potsie Webber
Ralph Malph
Chachi Arcola
Chuck Cunningham

Arnold

Bobby

Tommy

Jenny Piccalo

Ashley Pfister

Heather Pfister

Leather Tuscadero

STAR TREK (The Original)

Capt. Kirk

Mr. Spock

Dr. Leonard 'Bones' McCoy

Mr. Sulu

Lt. Uhura

Montgomery 'Scotty' Scott

Nurse Christine Chapel

Ensign Pavel Chekov

Yeoman Janice Rand

The Romulans

The Klingons

THUNDERBIRDS

Jeff Tracy

Scott Tracy (T1)

Virgil Tracy (T2)

Alan Tracy (T3)

Gordon Tracy (T4)

John Tracy (T5)

Lady Penelope Creighton-Ward

Aloysius Parker

Brains

Tin-Tin Kyrano

The Hood

Kyrano

Grandma

MASH

Capt. 'Hawkeye' Pierce

Capt. 'Trapper' McIntyre

Margaret 'Hot Lips' Houlihan

Major Frank Burns

Cpl. 'Radar' O'Reilly

Lt. Col. Henry Blake

Father Francis Mulchay

Sgt. Max Klinger

Col. Sherman T Potter

Capt. B J Hunnicut

Mjr. Charles Winchester III

THE MUPPETS

Kermit the Frog

Miss Piggy

a test of character

Fozzie Bear

Zoot

Gonzo

Statler

Waldorf

Sweetums

Sam the Eagle

The Swedish Chef

Dr Teeth

Sgt Floyd Pepper

Rowlf

Animal

Scooter

Beaker

Dr Julius Strangepork

Dr Bunsen Honeydew

Beauregard

Pops

Lew Zealand

Rizzo the Rat

Robin the Frog

Spamela Hamderson

Bill the Bubble Guy

Marge Simpson

Bart Simpson

Lisa Simpson

Maggie Simpson

Mr Montgomery Burns

Waylon Smithers

Moe Syslak

Principal Skinner

Patty Bouvier

Selma Bouvier

Ned Flanders

Milhouse Van Houten

Krusty the Clown

Apu Nahasapeemapetilon

Police Chief Wiggum

THE SIMPSONS

Homer Simpson

animal crackers

In this category you must come up with the names of famous animals. They can be real or fictitious but, if fictitious, they must have been portrayed on tv or film by real animals, cartoon characters are not allowed.

We have included some racehorses but it is a good idea to limit them by just including the most famous. You can let the people you are playing with decide on what is the definition of 'most famous'. Good Luck!

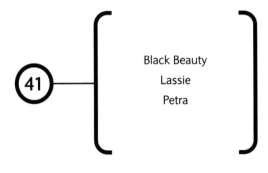

41

Black Beauty
Lassie
Petra

animal crackers

Arkle *(Racehorse)*

Babe *(Pig from the film)*

Beethoven *(Dog from the film)*

Ben *(Michael Jackson's rat)*

Bullseye *(Bill Sykes' dog)*

Champion *(The wonder horse)*

Cheetah *(Tarzan's friend)*

Chi Chi *(The giant panda)*

Clarence *(The cross eyed lion)*

Digby *(Dog from the film)*

DC *(That darn cat)*

Eddie *(Dog in Frasier)*

Freda *(Blue Peter tortoise)*

Flicka *(TV horse)*

Flipper *(Dolphin)*

Freeway *(Hart to Hart dog)*

Goldie *(Blue Peter dog)*

Guy *(The gorilla)*

Hammy *(Hamster)*

Humphrey *(No 10's cat)*

Jason *(Blue Peter cat)*

Kes *(Brit film kestrel)*

King Kong *(Giant gorilla)*

Kangaroo Jack *(From the film)*

Moby Dick *(White whale)*

Mr Ed *(Talking horse)*

Old Yeller *(Disney movie)*

Pickles *(Found World Cup)*

Red Rum *(Racehorse)*

Shep *(Blue Peter dog)*

Shergar *(Racehorse)*

Silver *(Lone Ranger's horse)*

Skippy *(The bush kangaroo)*

Socks *(The Whitehouse cat)*

Toto *(Wizard of Oz dog)*

Trigger *(Roy Rogers' horse)*

Well'ard *(Eastenders dog)*

Willy *(Whale)*

men in black

Villains, baddies, sworn enemies and all round bad guys, this hall of infamy will send a chill down your spine.

The characters must be fictitious but apart from that anything goes, so, if they are up to no good they can go on your list. Make sure you include the show or film they come from in your answers.

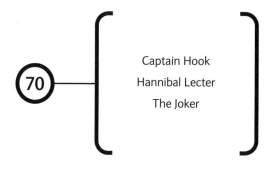

70

Captain Hook
Hannibal Lecter
The Joker

men in black

Agent Smith	*Matrix*
Alex Forest	*Fatal Attraction*
Annie Wilkes	*Misery*
Baron Greenback	*Danger Mouse*
Barry Grant	*Brookside*
Bill Sykes	*Oliver*
Bill The Butcher	*Gangs of New York*
Blofeld	*James Bond*
Bluto & Brutus	*Popeye*
Bookworm	*Batman*
Captain Black	*Captain Scarlet*
Captain Zargon	*Action Man*
Casanova Frankenstein	*Mystery Men*
Catwoman	*Batman*
Chucky	*Childs Play*
Cuella de Vil	*101 Dalmations*
Commodus	*Gladiator*
Count Dracula	*Dracula*
Darth Maul	*Star Wars*
Darth Vador	*Star Wars*
Dr Evil	*Austin Powers*
Dr No	*James Bond*
Dr X	*Action Man*
Dr Zachary Smith	*Lost in Space*
Edgar	*Men in Black*
Egghead	*Batman*

Freddy Kruegar. . . . . *Nightmare on Elm Street*

Goldfinger & Odd Job. . . . . *James Bond*

Gollum. . . . . *Lord of the Rings*

Hans Gruber. . . . . *Die Hard*

Hugo Drax & Jaws. . . . . *James Bond*

Lady Tremaine. . . . . *Cinderella*

Maleficent. . . . . *Sleeping Beauty*

Moriarty. . . . . *Sherlock Holmes*

Norman Bates . . . . *Psycho*

Kano. . . . . *Mortal Combat*

Jack Torrance. . . . . *The Shining*

Jason Voorhees. . . . . *Friday The 13th*

King Tut. . . . . *Batman*

Leatherface . . . . *Texas Chainsaw Massacre*

Lex Luther. . . . . *Superman*

Lord Farquaad . . . . *Shrek*

Lucius Malfoy. . . . . *Harry Potter*

Magneto. . . . . *X-Men*

Michael Myers. . . . . *Halloween*

Ming The Merciless. . . . . *Flash Gordon*

Mr Blonde. . . . . *Reservoir Dogs*

Nick Cotton. . . . . *Eastenders*

Patrick Bateman. . . . . *American Psycho*

Pinhead. . . . . *Hellraiser*

Richard Hillman. . . . . *Coronation Street*

Scar . . . . *The Lion King*

men in black

Scaramanga & Nick Nack. . . . . *James Bond*

Sheriff of Nottingham. . . . . *Robin Hood*

Stromboli. . . . . *Pinnochio*

Sylvester Sneakly. . . . . *The Perils of Penelope Pitstop*

Terminator . . . . *Terminator*

Titan. . . . . *Stingray*

Trevor Morgan . . . . *Eastenders*

The Hood. . . . . *Thunderbirds*

The Evil Queen. . . . . *Snow White*

The Green Goblin. . . . . *Spiderman*

The Mysterons. . . . . *Captain Scarlet*

The Penguin. . . . . *Batman*

The Riddler. . . . . *Batman*

THRUSH. . . . . *The Man From UNCLE*

Wicked Witch of the West. . . . . *The Wizard of Oz*

go go go

All you need to do for this category is think of short, well known phrases that begin with the word GO. How you define 'well known' is up to you and is bound to cause some argument but as an example 'go to town' is perfectly acceptable whereas 'go on the bus' is just a sentence with go in.

So go get 'em.

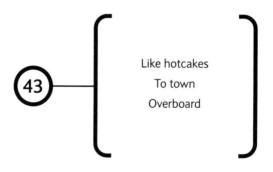

43

Like hotcakes
To town
Overboard

go go go

About	Public
Ahead	Scot Free
Begging	Steady
Belly up	The distance
Between	Through the mill
Bust	Through the roof
By the board	To pieces
By the wayside	To seed
Crazy	To the dogs
Dutch	Under
Easy	Up in flames
For broke	Up in smoke
For It	Without
For the jugular	Without saying
Getter	
Halves	
In to bat	
It alone	
Like the wind	
Off the deep end	
On	
On record	
On the warpath	
One better	
Out of your way	
Places	

what's the situation?

Lots to choose from in this category and always good fun remembering some of the great tv sitcoms that have made us laugh over the years.

We have only included British programmes but you could include America if you wanted to, there have been some classic programmes from the other side of the Atlantic.

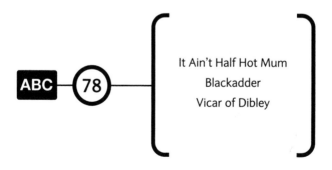

ABC — (78) —

It Ain't Half Hot Mum
Blackadder
Vicar of Dibley

what's the situation?

Absolutely Fabulous . . . .*Edina and Patsy*

A Fine Romance. . . . .*Laura Dalton and Mike Selway*

'Allo 'Allo . . . . *Rene and Edith Artois*

Are You Being Served . . .*Mrs Slocombe and Mr Humphries*

As Time Goes By. . . . .*Jean and Lionel*

Birds of a Feather . . . .*Sharon, Tracey and Dorien*

Bless This House. . . . .*Sid Abbott and Family*

Bottom . . . .*Richie Richard and Eddie Hitler*

Brass . . . .*Bradley Hardacre and Family*

Bread . . . .*Nelly Boswell and Family*

The Brittas Empire. . . . .*Gordon Brittas and the Team*

Butterflies. . . . .*Ria, Ben and Family*

Citizen Smith. . . . .*Wolfie Smith and Ken*

Coupling . . . .*Steve, Jane, Susan, Sally, Patrick and Jeff*

Dad's Army . . . . *Capt. Mainwaring and his platoon*

Desmonds . . . . *Desmond, Shirley and Pork Pie*

Dinnerladies. . . . .*Bren, Dolly, Anita and Twinkle*

Doctor in the House . . .*Michael Upton and Duncan Waring*

Drop the Dead Donkey. . . . . .*Gus Hedges and George Dent*

The Dustbinmen . . . . . . *'Cheese and Egg', Winston and Eric*

Duty Free . . . .*David and Amy Pearce*

Ever Decreasing Circles. . . . *Martin, Ann, Howard and Hilda*

Fall and Rise of Reginald Perrin . . . . *Reggie, Joan and CJ*

Father Dear Father . . . .*Patrick Glover, Anna and Karen*

Father Ted . . . . *Fathers Ted, Dougal and Jack*

Fawlty Towers . . . .*Basil, Sybil, Polly and Manuel*

Fresh Fields . . . . *William and Hester Fields*

George and Mildred. . . . . *George and Mildred Roper*

Gimme Gimme Gimme. . . . . *Linda and Tom*

The Good Life . . . . *The Goods and The Leadbetters*

Goodnight Sweetheart . . . . *Gary Sparrow*

Hancock's Half Hour. . . . . *Tony Hancock and Sid James*

Hi De Hi . . . . *Jeffrey Fairbrother and Gladys Pugh*

I'm Alan Partridge. . . . . *Alan Partridge and Lynn*

Just Good Friends. . . . . *Vince and Penny*

Keeping Up Appearances . . . . *Hyacinth and Richard Bucket*

Last of the Summer Wine. . . . . . . *Clegg, Compo and Foggy*

The League of Gentlemen . . *The residents of Royston Vasey*

The Likely Lads . . . . *Terry and Bob*

The Liver Birds. . . . . *Beryl, Sandra and Dawn*

Love Thy Neighbour . . . . *Eddie Booth and Bill Reynolds*

Man About the House . . . . *Robin, Chrissy and Jo*

May to December . . . *Alec Callender, Miss Flood and Hilary*

Men Behaving Badly . . . . . *Gary, Tony, Deborah and Dorothy*

My Family . . . . *The Harper Family*

My Wife Next Door. . . . . *George and Suzy Bassett*

The New Statesman. . . . . *Alan Bastard and Piers*

The Office. . . . . *David Brent, Gareth and Tim*

On the Buses . . . . *Butler, Arthur, Blakey and Olive*

One Foot In The Grave . . . . *Victor Meldrew*

Only Fools and Horses . . . . *Del Boy and Rodney*

Open All Hours . . . . *Arkwright and Granville*

what's the situation?

Phoenix Nights . . . . *Brian Potter and Jerry 'St Clair' Dignan*

Please Sir. . . . . .*Mr Hedges, Frankie Abbot and classmates*

Porridge . . . . *Fletcher, Godber and Mackay*

Rab C Nesbitt. . . . . *Rab C Nesbitt*

Red Dwarf . . . .*Rimmer, Lister, Cat and Kryten*

Rising Damp . . . .*Rigsby, Alan, Phillip and Miss Jones*

Robin's Nest . . . . *Robin Tripp and Vicky*

The Royle Family . . . . *Jim, Barbara, Denise and Anthony*

A Sharp Intake of Breath . . . . *Peter and Sheila Barnes*

Shelley . . . .*James Shelley and Fran*

Some Mothers Do 'Ave 'Em . . . .*Frank and Betty*

Sorry . . . .*Timothy Lumsden*

Steptoe and Son . . . . *Harold and Albert*

Sykes. . . . .*Eric, Hattie and Chalkie*

Terry and June . . . .*Terry and June Medford*

The Thin Blue Line . . *Insp. Raymond Fowler and PC Goodie*

Til Death Us Do Part . . . .*Alf Garnet and family*

To the Manor Born . . . .*Audrey Fforbes Hamilton*

2 point 4 Children. . . . .*Bill and Ben Porter*

Up Pompeii . . . . *Lurcio, Ludicrus Sextus and Erotica*

Waiting For God. . . . . *Diana and Tom*

Yes Minister. . . . .*Jim Hacket, Sir Humphrey and Bernard*

The Young Ones. . . . . *Rick, Neil, Vyvyan and Mike*

capital ideas

This will sort out who was listening in geography lessons. There are actually well over 200 capital cities in the world and while, of course, some are better known than others, with so much international news on the tv these days everyone should know a good few answers.

Make sure you get the country as well as the capital.

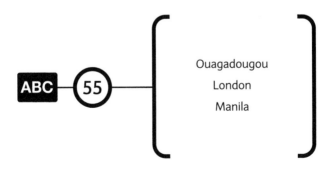

ABC — 55

Ouagadougou
London
Manila

capital ideas

Algiers . . . . *Algeria*	Lima. . . . .*Peru*
Amman . . . .*Jordan*	Lisbon. . . . .*Portugal*
Athens . . . . *Greece*	Luxembourg. . . *Luxembourg*
Baghdad . . . . *Iraq*	Madrid. . . . .*Spain*
Bangkok. . . . . *Thailand*	Mexico City. . . . .*Mexico*
Bern. . . . . *Switzerland*	Monaco. . . . .*Monaco*
Bucharest. . . . .*Romania*	Nairobi. . . . .*Kenya*
Budapest . . . .*Hungary*	Nicosia. . . . . *Cyprus*
Buenos Aires . . . . *Argentina*	New Delhi . . . . *India*
Brasilia . . . .*Brazil*	Oslo. . . . . *Norway*
Bridgetown . . . . . . *Barbados*	Ottawa . . . .*Canada*
Cairo . . . .*Egypt*	Phnom Penh . . . . *Cambodia*
Canberra. . . . . *Australia*	Port-au-Prince . . . .*Haiti*
Colombo. . . . . *Sri Lanka*	Riga. . . . .*Latvia*
Copenhagen . . . . . *Denmark*	Rome . . . .*Italy*
Damascus. . . . .*Syria*	Singapore. . . . . . . *Singapore*
Dublin . . . .*Ireland*	Sofia . . . .*Bulgaria*
Freetown. . . . . *Sierra Leone*	Stockholm. . . . .*Sweden*
Georgetown. . . . . . .*Guyana*	Tehran . . . . *Iran*
Harare. . . . . *Zimbabwe*	Tripoli. . . . .*Libya*
Helsinki . . . . *Finland*	Ulan Bator . . . . . . *Mongolia*
Islamabad. . . . . *Pakistan*	Valletta . . . .*Malta*
Kabul . . . . *Afghanistan*	Warsaw. . . . . *Poland*
Khartoum. . . . .*Sudan*	Washington DC. . . . . . .*USA*
Katmandou. . . . .*Nepal*	Wellington. . . . *New Zealand*
Kuala Lumpur . . . . *Malaysia*	Zagreb . . . .*Croatia*

junior choice

"Hello children everywhere", the immortal words of David McCulloch (Uncle Mac) as he introduced Children's Favourites every Saturday morning from 1954-1967. Then it was the turn of Ed (Stewpot) Stewart on Junior Choice to keep some of those old songs alive.

Very evocative for all of us of a 'certain age', how many songs from Junior Choice can you remember?

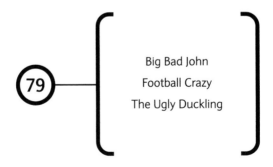

(79)

Big Bad John
Football Crazy
The Ugly Duckling

junior choice

A Four Legged Friend. . . . . *Roy Rogers*

A Windmill In Amsterdam . . . . *Ronnie Wilton*

All Things Bright and Beautiful . . . . *Uncle Mac*

All I want for Christmas . . . . *Max Bygraves*

Any Old Iron . . . . *Peter Sellers*

Ballad of Davy Crockett . . . .*'Tennessee' Ernie Ford*

Bangers and Mash . . . . *Peter Sellers & Sophia Loren*

The Bee Song . . . .*Arthur Askey*

Beep Beep (The Bubble Car Song) . . . .*The Playmates*

The Big Rock Candy Mountain . . . . *Burl Ives*

Boom oo Yattata . . . . *Morecambe and Wise*

The Deadwood Stage . . . .*Doris Day*

Does Your Chewing Gum Lose It's Flavour. *Lonnie Donegan*

Down Came The Rain . . . .*Mister Murray*

Flash Bang Wallop . . . .*Tommy Steele*

Gilly Gilly Ossenfeffer . . . .*Max Bygraves*

Goodness Gracious Me . . . .*Peter Sellers & Sophia Loren*

Grandfather's Clock . . . .*Radio Revellers*

Hello Muddah . . . .*Allan Sherman*

Henery the Eighth I Am . . . .*Herman's Hermits*

Hippopotamus song . . . .*Flanders & Swann*

Hole in the Ground . . . .*Bernard Cribbins*

How Much is That Doggie? . . . .*Pinky & Perky*

I'm A Gnu . . . .*Flanders and Swann*

I Taut I Taw a Puddy Cat . . . . *Mel Blanc*

In an English Country Garden . . . .*Jimmie Rodgers*

I've Got No Strings. . . . . .Dickie Jones

I've Lost My Mummy . . . .*Rolf Harris*

Jake the Peg . . . .*Rolf Harris*

The King's New Clothes . . . . *Danny Kaye*

Laughing Policeman . . . . *Charles Penrose*

Lily the Pink . . . .*The Scaffold*

Little White Bull . . . . *Tommy Steele*

Little Sir Echo . . . . *Max Bygraves*

Me and My Teddy Bear . . . .*Rosemary Clooney*

Messing About On The River . . . .*Josh McRae*

Mole in a Hole . . . . *The Southlanders*

Mommy, Gimme a Drinka Water . . . .*Danny Kaye*

My Boomerang Won't Come Back . . . .*Charlie Drake*

My Brother . . . . *Terry Scott*

My Old Man's A Dustman . . . . *Lonnie Donegan*

Nellie the Elephant . . . . *Mandy Miller*

Owl and the Pussycat . . . .*Elton Hayes*

Poppa Piccolino . . . .*Petula Clark*

Puff the Magic Dragon . . . . *Peter, Paul and Mary*

Puffin' Billy . . . . *Melody Light Orchestra*

Ragtime Cowboy Joe . . . . *The Chipmunks*

Right Said Fred . . . . *Bernard Cribbins*

Robin Hood . . . .*Dick James*

Run Rabbit Run. . . . .*Flannagan & Allen*

Runaway train . . . . *Vernon Delhart*

She'll be Coming Round the Mountain . . . .*Trad*

Soldier Soldier Won't You Marry Me? . . . . . . *Jimmie Rodgers*

Sparky's Magic Piano . . . . *Danny Kay*

Swinging on a Star . . . . *Frank Sinatra*

Teddy Bear's Picnic . . . . *Henry Hall*

Thank You Very Much . . . . *The Scaffold*

The Animals Went In Two-by-Two . . . . *Trad*

Three Billy Goats Gruff . . . . *Frank Luther*

Three Little Fishes . . . . *Frankie Howerd*

Three Wheels On My Wagon . . . *The New Christy Minstrels*

Thumbelina . . . . *Danny Kaye*

Tie Me Kangaroo Down . . . . *Rolf Harris*

Tubby the Tuba . . . . *Danny Kaye*

Tulips from Amsterdam. . . . .*Max Bygraves*

Two Little Boys . . . .*Rolf Harris*

The Ugly Bug Ball . . . . *Burl Ives*

Ugly Duckling . . . . *Bernard Cribbins*

When I See an Elepahnt Fly . . . . *Clive Peterson*

Where's Me Shirt? . . . .*Ken Dodd*

Who's Afraid of the Big Bad Wolf ?. . . . .*Pinky & Perky*

Wonderful Wonderful Copenhagen . . . . *Danny Kaye*

Woody Woodpecker . . . .*Mel Blanc*

Yellow Rose of Texas . . . .*Stan Freburg*

You Need Hands . . . .*Max Bygraves*

You're a Pink Toothbrush . . . . *Max Bygraves*

songs for the asking

Quite simply any song with a title that has a question mark after it.

If you want to be difficult you could ask for the artistes as well as the songs and, as usual, if there is any doubt about an answer a rendition of the song is always a good test.

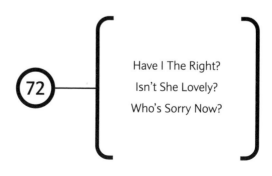

72

Have I The Right?
Isn't She Lovely?
Who's Sorry Now?

songs for the asking

Ain't She Sweet? . . . . *Jack Yellen*

Ain't That A Shame? . . . . *Fats Domino*

Are You Lonesome Tonight? . . . . *Elvis Presley*

Can You Be True? . . . . *Elvis Costello*

Could It Be Forever? . . . . *David Cassidy*

Could It Be I'm Falling In Love? . . . . *Detroit Spinners*

Didn't I Blow Your Mind? . . . . *The Delfonics*

Didn't We Almost Have It All? . . . . *Whitney Houston*

Do They Know It's Christmas? . . . . *Band Aid*

Do Ya Think I'm Sexy? . . . . *Rod Stewart*

Do You Know the Way to San Jose? . . . . . . *Dionne Warwick*

Do You Know What I Mean? . . . . *Oasis*

Do You Know Where You Going To? . . . . *Diana Ross*

Do You Really Want to Hurt Me? . . . . *Culture Club*

Do You Wanna Dance? . . . . *Bobby Freeman*

Do You Wanna Know A Secret? . . . . *The Beatles*

Do You Wanna Touch Me? . . . . *Joan Jett*

Does Your Mother Know? . . . . *Abba*

Don't It Make My Brown Eyes Blue? . . . . *Crystal Gale*

Don't You Want Me? . . . . *The Human League*

Have I Told You Lately That I Love You? . . . . . . *Van Morrison*

Have You Ever Had It Blue? . . . . *The Style Council*

Have You Seen Her? . . . . *The Chi Lites*

How Am I Supposed to Live Without You? . . *Michael Bolton*

How Can You Mend a Broken Heart? . . . . *The Bee Gees*

How Deep Is Your Love? . . . . *The Bee Gees*

How Long?. . . . . *Ace*

If I Said You Had a Beautiful Body?. . . *The Bellamy Brothers*

Is She Really Going Out With Him? . . . . *Joe Jackson*

Is That Love?. . . . .*Squeeze*

Is There Anybody Out There?. . . . . *Pink Floyd*

Is There Something I Should Know?. . . . . *Duran Duran*

Is This Love? . . . . *Bob Marley*

Isn't Life Strange? . . . .*The Moody Blues*

Should I Stay Or Should I Go? . . . .*The Clash*

What Are You Doing Sunday? . . . . *Dawn*

What Becomes of the Broken Hearted? . . . . . . *Jimmy Ruffin*

What Do You Want? . . . . *Adam Faith*

What Do You Wanna Make Those Eyes? . . .*Shakin' Stevens*

What Kind Of Fool Am I? . . . . *Shirley Bassey*

What Have I Done To Deserve This? . . . .*Pet Shop Boys*

What Have I Got To Do To Make You Love Me?. . *Elton John*

What's Going On? . . . . *Marvin Gaye*

What's Love Got To Do With It? . . . . *Tina Turner*

What Now, My Love? . . . .*Shirley Bassey*

What Took You So Long?. . . . . *Emma Bunton*

What's New Pussycat?. . . . . *Tom Jones*

When Will I Be Famous? . . . . *Bros*

When Will I See You Again?. . . . . *The Three Degrees*

Where Did Our Love Go? . . . .*Diana Ross*

Where Do Broken Hearts Go? . . . . *Whitney Houston*

Where Is The Love? . . . . *Roberta Flack*

songs for the asking

Who Are You? . . . . *The Who*

Where Do You Go To, My Lovely? . . . . *Peter Starstedt*

Whodunnit? . . . . *Tavares*

Who Do You Think You Are? . . . . *The Spice Girls*

Who Let The Dogs Out? . . . . *Baha Men*

Who Loves You? . . . . *The Four Seasons*

Who Put The Bomp? . . . . *The Viscounts*

Who's That Girl? . . . . *The Eurythmics*

Who's Zoomin Who? . . . . *Aretha Franklin*

Why? . . . . *Donny Osmond*

Why'd You Lie To Me? . . . . *Anastacia*

Why Can't This Be Love? . . . . *Van Halen*

Why Do Fools Fall In Love?. *Frankie Lyman & The Teenagers*

Why Does It Always Rain On Me? . . . . *Travis*

Will You Still Love Me Tomorrow? . . . . *The Shirelles*

Would I Lie To You? . . . . *The Eurythmics*

Wouldn't It Be Nice? . . . . *The Beach Boys*

what's cooking?

Or rather, how is it cooked? This category includes everything a chef might legitimately do to your food before it is served up on the table.

Ready, steady, cook!

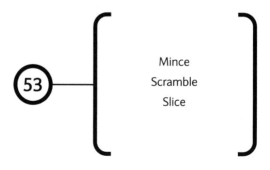

53 [Mince
Scramble
Slice]

what's cooking?

Bake	Jug
Barbecue	Jullienne
Batter	Knead
Beat	Marinate
Blanche	Mash
Boil	Microwave
Braise	Pluck
Broil	Poach
Carve	Poche Grill
Chargrill	Pot Roast
Chop	Roast
Coddle	Sauté
Cream	Seal
Crush	Sear
Deep Fry	Season
Devil	Skin
Dice	Slice
Fillet	Simmer
Flambé	Steam
Fold	Stew
Fricassé	Stir Fry
Fry	Tenderize
Glaze	Toast
Grate	Whisk
Griddle	
Grill	

blue peter badge

The list contains presenters and pets from the legendary children's tv series and if you can remember them all you really do deserve a Blue Peter badge.

Of course you could go for a gold Blue Peter badge by putting them in the correct date order.

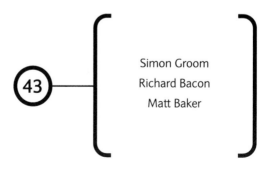

blue peter badge

Christopher Trace	*The Dogs*
Leila Williams	Petra
Anita West	Patch
Valerie Singleton	Shep
John Noakes	Goldie
Peter Purves	Bonnie
Lesley Judd	
Christopher Wenner	*The Cats*
Tina Heath	Jason
Sarah Greene	Jack
Peter Duncan	Jill
Janet Ellis	Willow
Michael Sundin	
Mark Curry	*The Tortoises*
Caron Keating	Freda
Yvette Fielding	Maggie
John Leslie	Jim
Diane-Louise Jordan	
Anthea Turner	*The Parrots*
Tim Vincent	Joey
Romana D'Annunzio	Barney
Stuart Miles	
Katy Hill	
Konnie Huq	
Simon Thomas	
Liz Barker	

mellow yellow

The answers must be things that are either always yellow, like bananas, or traditionally coloured yellow, like a duster. This is also a category where you can think laterally as long as yellow is an integral and recognised part of the answer like Yellow Submarine.

Always remember to make sure that the answers you accept are predominantly yellow and do not just have some yellow in them.

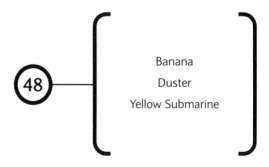

48
Banana
Duster
Yellow Submarine

mellow yellow

Baby Chick

Butter

Buttercups

Canary

Cheese

Corn on the cob

Cowardice

Coventry football shirt

Custard

Daffodils

Dandelion

Egg Nog

Egg Yolk

English Mustard

F1 Flag

Grapefruit

Jaundice

Lemon

Lemon Curd

Marigolds

Marmite jar lid

McDonalds M

New York Taxi

Oilskins

Pollen

Post It Notes

Rear number plate

Refs card

Rose of Texas

Rubber Duck

Sherbet Lemons

Sponge

Sun

Sunflowers

Tennis Balls

Yellow Brick Road

Yellow Fever

Yellow Jersey (Cycling)

Yellow Lines

Yellow Pages

Yellow Pepper

Yellow River (Song)

Monopoly

Leicester Sq

Coventry Street

Piccadilly

state of the union

The United States is a big country and there are fifty of them to choose from.

How many can you remember?

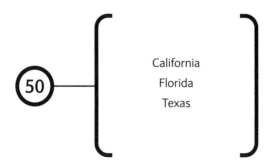

state of the union

Alabama	New Hampshire
Alaska	New Jersey
Arizona	New Mexico
Arkansas	New York
Colorado	North Carolina
Connecticut	North Dakota
Delaware	Ohio
Georgia	Oklahoma
Hawaii	Oregon
Idaho	Pennsylvania
Illinois	Rhode Island
Indiana	South Carolina
Iowa	South Dakota
Kansas	Tennessee
Kentucky	Utah
Louisiana	Vermont
Maine	Virginia
Maryland	Washington
Massachusetts	West Virginia
Michigan	Wisconsin
Minnesota	Wyoming
Mississippi	
Missouri	
Montana	
Nebraska	
Nevada	

notes

www.alienzulu.co.uk